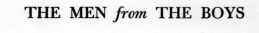

# THE MEN *from* THE BOYS

*Books by Perrin Stryker*

THE MEN FROM THE BOYS

A GUIDE TO MODERN MANAGEMENT METHODS
(with the Editors of *Fortune*)

ARMS AND THE AFTERMATH

PERRIN STRYKER

# THE MEN
# *from* THE BOYS

*Harper & Brothers* — NEW YORK

# Contents

# Foreword

THIS BOOK was written to be read by anyone who is interested in improving his understanding of human qualities, including, of course, his own. It is basically a collection of stories dealing with certain traits that have been commonly ascribed to able, mature people in industrial management. To a very large extent this is a work of fictionalized fact, based directly on research and my observation of managers and executives over many years in my capacity as an editor of *Fortune* magazine. The situations, the comments, the ideas, and the conclusions presented are drawn predominantly from those found in studying real-life corporations and their personnel. However, while the chapter on leadership includes the names and case histories of several notable American businessmen, all other characters in this book, and practically all the names of corporations mentioned, are imaginary, and are not intended to resemble any real-life people or corporations.

By resorting to the techniques of fiction it has been possible to present many aspects of executive life that are commonly glossed over in addition to those that escape general attention. The devices of fiction proved especially useful for illustrating the qualities and traits dealt with. Several reasons for this will be apparent to anyone who has had much

to do with people in management; to those who have but
slightly experienced such people it should be clear that fictionalized managers and executives can be presented far
more simply and clearly than their individually complex,
real-life counterparts.

The origin of these stories was a series on executive qualities which I wrote for *Fortune* in 1958-59. Four of the
fictionalized presentations published in that series are included in this book as Chapters 2, 4, 7, and 9; for permission
to present these copyrighted stories I am indebted to *Fortune's* publisher, Ralph D. Paine, Jr. I am also grateful to
Hedley Donovan, Duncan Norton-Taylor and Jay Gold, the
*Fortune* editors under whom the series on qualities was prepared. I wish, however, to clear *Fortune* of all responsibility
for the material and presentation of the seven new chapters
which are included in this book. Similarly I want to express
my appreciation formally to Evan Thomas, my editor at
Harper's, whose enthusiasm for this approach to the executive life persuaded me to take a leave of absence in
order to extend the original series. And I respectfully acknowledge that there are certain observations and views expressed in this book, particularly in the final chapter, to
which some of the Harper editors and officers (including
Thomas) are strongly opposed.

To the many, many others whose confidences and cooperation over the years have made this book possible, I here
express especial gratitude and appreciation.

With these acknowledgments I wish now to address myself to those students of management who have acquired a
serious interest in the relatively new process of "executive
development." The following paragraphs will, I earnestly
hope, help to clarify the intentions of this book.

The historical significance of the full-grown executive can

only be dimly appreciated. He is the remarkable—and still remarkably rare—product of a process that is itself history-making. Indeed the twentieth century might be recorded as the epoch in which men for the first time attempted to cultivate, methodically and on a large scale, a class of superior managers. This is no slight matter. The serious effort expended today in large corporations to find and develop those who can expertly manage (which includes helping others to develop as managers) is potentially a more beneficial lesson for mankind than all the wonders of scientific technology. For when the process of executive development is seriously undertaken it should eventually demonstrate that a well-developed executive is one who possesses the qualities of a well-developed individual. What is even more important, the encouragement of executive maturity should promote, both within and without the ranks of management, a clearer understanding of the virtues that organization can nurture in the individual.

These are abiding virtues, though for centuries they have been derided by the partisans of individualism. The workings of the large corporation today are, certainly, full of pitfalls for the individualist. Such risks as thoughtless conformity to the mores of a corporation and reverence for group opinion have lately been pointed out by many earnest students of management; thus a former *Fortune* colleague of mine, William H. Whyte, Jr., author of *The Organization Man,* has pictured the risks so vividly that many now seem to assume that the organization is, inevitably, an enemy of modern man. I do not assume that. On the basis of my observations of managers and executives, it is not organization that deforms the individual: poor management does that, and poor management is the product of poorly developed managers.

Organization and managers are essentially the complementary parts of management: the hard struggle that managers go through in learning to achieve good organization can contribute powerfully to their own development. A good executive, in short, might be described as an individual who has demonstrated that his own development is both a product and a function of organization.

This is more than can be claimed for the objectives of management training today. Intense efforts to develop executives in recent years have aimed at finding and training personalities who fit the organization, who get along with others, who exhibit a variety of other traits that others in the corporation consider desirable. Executive development is still largely a personality hunt spurred on by immediate considerations, such as the expansion of a company, the specialization of its functions, or the loss of its top officers. In time, however, the development of executive talents could become more than a practical operating requirement; it could become recognized as a basic corporate function in itself. Ensuring the supply of superior managers would ensure the smooth development of organization, which in turn would secure the productive continuity of the corporation.

It promises to be a considerable time before executive development achieves this commanding importance. So far, the process has merely passed through some preliminary stages since the 1930's, when top managers first generally recognized that management skill involves a good deal more than rugged individualistic dominance backed by the authority to fire and hire. One stage has seen the rise of the "human relations" approach to problems caused by faulty organization and deficient managers; another stage has brought a vast increase in training and managerial techniques, with scores of thousands of managers now attending schools, seminars, and conferences.

Yet in all this activity one critical weakness remains: there is still no accurate means of judging managerial performance and potential. It is still not possible, by any test or technique, to select the particular manager who will, now or later, give the best performance on a particular job. The most definite fact that the psychological testing seems to have revealed is that managerial success is not determined primarily by aptitudes (e.g., intelligence), or by proficiencies (e.g., technical know-how), but by individual traits (e.g., initiative, dependability, integrity). And the big questions for management remain: how are such traits recognized, and how are they developed?

In trying to find some of the answers to these questions I soon discovered that the search for personality traits was passé. Many who had tried to identify the "essential" traits of an executive had abandoned the effort; there seemed to be no possible agreement about traits that could be counted characteristic of able executives. But at the same time I found that almost no effort had been made to find out what managers and executives themselves meant when they attributed qualities or traits to their subordinates. I assumed they probably meant many different things, but proposed to find out. Through extensive interviews and questionnaires involving more than 150 high-ranking management men over a period of many months, I learned how fully justified my assumption was: every one of fourteen commonly used traits turned out, as defined by these men, to embrace an extraordinary complexity of meanings. For instance, the written definitions of dependability alone, which 75 of these men supplied, included no fewer than 147 different concepts.

Such diversity of understanding does not, in my judgment, mean that the ideas these men hold about certain human traits are a babel of confusion. To me it is evidence that the range of their understanding is far broader and more subtly differentiated than has been generally supposed. In view of this diversity it seems clear that the road to better understanding of personality traits does not lead to simplification, generalization, and common definitions. On the contrary, the real understanding of such traits inevitably requires the capacity for discriminating among subtle differences and degrees of human behavior. And the judging of such traits in oneself, as well as in others, can become the critical test of individual competence—which is also executive competence. I sincerely hope that the chapters in this book will induce the thoughtful reader to agree.

PERRIN STRYKER

# THE MEN *from* THE BOYS

CHAPTER ONE      *Talk of*

*Executives*

As I STEPPED off the elevator and walked into the big dining room of the Midtown Club, I saw my old friend Phil Cadmus at once, sitting, as he so often did, at a nearby corner table. He was talking with a couple of men I had never seen before but who were clearly either his clients or potential clients. Cadmus I knew as a man who rarely wastes a lunch hour. A former psychology professor turned management consultant, he has more than once reminded me that he does more business in a year over food and drink than he has ever done over all the desks he has ever sat behind. His guests today, I noted, were already well started on their cocktails, and I could see that Cadmus, while sipping his usual bourbon on the rocks, was studying the faces of the two men as both leaned forward over their luncheon menus. I had seen Cadmus do this before, and thought it would be interesting to explore this little technique of his someday when I was alone with him. He was rather proud of his ability to judge people, and had once, I recall, made quite a hobby of face-reading. Something he told me about the "buffers" he always found in a real executive's jowls came back to me; and there was also something about the "aggression" in a man showing up in the jutting bridge of his nose—the more Roman the more aggressive, apparently. I was reflecting on some interesting

conclusions that might be drawn from this when I realized
that Cadmus had spotted me and was beckoning me over to
his table. This could only mean that his guests were reliable,
well-established clients, for he was always careful about iso-
lating both new and prospective clients. Since his great skill
as a management consultant had been repeatedly demonstrated over a good many years, and since my business is the
study of men in management, I gladly accepted the opening
Cadmus now offered. It turned out to be very rewarding.

Cadmus introduced me first to the older of the two men
with him, Gerald Cranford, a man about sixty, I judged, who
looked just a trifle worn. His casual, pleasant manner of
greeting me momentarily effaced this impression, but after
we had shaken hands that faint look of steady fatigue returned, and I was sure that he had somewhat more than the
usual share of worries, business or otherwise. Cranford's
well-cut suit and conservative tie suggested that he was no
newcomer to executive ranks, a point shortly supported by
Cadmus' explanation that "Gerry, as you undoubtedly know,
is senior vice president of General Products." I didn't know
this, but as soon as I heard Cadmus use the word "undoubtedly," I realized that Gerald Cranford was probably a man
who was not so well known outside his company as he would
like to be, and that Cadmus was expecting me to treat Cranford accordingly. It was a small price to pay for admission
to Cadmus' luncheon circle.

The second man was introduced as "Mr. Andrew Resch,
Division Manager of Ace Manufacturing." Resch was short
and heavy, with a long saturnine face from which his close-
set eyes bulged slightly, giving him a tense expression; at the
same time his relaxed manner made him seem just mildly
curious about whatever was in front of him. His handshake
was powerful and deliberate; I judged him to be in his late
forties, and his clothes and an awkward gesture (he tucked

his napkin in his coat pocket when he got up to greet me) marked him for me as an up-from-the-bottom, self-made manager. He was also, I was ready to bet, a good deal brighter about people than Cranford.

There was the familiar slight pause after I had sat down at the table, and after I'd ordered a drink, Cadmus apparently felt he had to assure his friends that I was not going to take down everything they said and rush it into print. He then went on to tell me something about the two men and the deal they had arrived at. It was nothing particularly special, as a deal, but I was grateful to Cadmus for his frankness. It seems that Cranford had called Cadmus in and asked him to start a manhunt for a division manager for General Products' Tennessee plant; the former manager had been plucked by General Products' biggest competitor, and Cranford wanted a replacement who wouldn't desert the company for the sake of what he called "a few more bucks."

At this point in Cadmus' narrative, Cranford spoke up. "I realize money is damned important to any manager," he said, "but I think a man ought to have enough loyalty to his company so that at least he gives his boss a chance to meet an outside bid." I sneaked a glance at Resch to see how he was taking this. I couldn't tell much, for he kept his eyes turned down on the half-empty cocktail glass in front of him. So I risked a question, and asked him if he thought loyalty to a company was something that could be retained by cash, as Cranford's comments seemed to imply. Resch smiled a little. "Sure," he said, "money can hold most people, except when a guy's got a special gripe against his boss, or gets a big chance at a bigger job." He looked over at Cranford and said, "I guess Mr. Cranford would agree that the salary he's offered me as division manager is part of the purchase price of my loyalty. But of course it's only part of the deal. I wouldn't be taking the job if I didn't think it had a future,

and if I didn't think Mr. Cranford would be an O.K. boss to
work with."

Cranford nodded, but said nothing, and Cadmus then finished off the rest of what he wanted to tell me about the deal.
His main point was that Cranford had been anxious to find a
very special manager, one who would come equipped with
"nearly all the schoolbook qualities." Cadmus had warned
Cranford that the paragon of a manager he was looking for
just didn't exist, and Cranford finally agreed to let Cadmus
submit the best available manager he could locate. Cadmus
said he had been perfectly confident of being able to find a
man who would please Cranford, and he sounded so confident that I suspected he had some private knowledge about
Cranford that allowed him to predict precisely the kind of
man Cranford would take to. I decided to play this hunch,
and asked Cadmus if he would be willing to name two or
three qualities he thought every manager ought to have.

"You can't catch me on that one," Cadmus replied. "As a
matter of fact I ought to feel offended by your asking that
question, but I'll excuse you on the grounds I was maybe asking for trouble when I asked you over here. Well, you should
know as well as I do that there's no set number of special and
definable qualities or abilities an executive has to have. In
spite of all the articles and books on how to identify executive talent, it's a terribly tough job."

Cranford looked a bit annoyed. "Nonsense," he said. "I'd
say any man who is really an executive can recognize good
managerial ability. Trouble with you fellows is that you're
always trying to analyze and define these things as if they
were chemicals that could be refined and then mixed into an
ideal compound. They can't be treated that way—but that
still doesn't mean an executive can't identify executive ability
in another man. If he's good, he can do this almost without
thinking about it—sort of by intuition, I guess."

Now it was Resch who looked faintly annoyed, but he didn't say anything. I had an idea, however, that he might be nudged into saying a good deal that Cranford wouldn't have expected him to say. Even by this time it was plain that Cranford didn't know Resch very well, and I wondered how Cadmus had sized up Resch as a man who could work with Cranford. I saw Cadmus watching Resch closely; then he turned and spoke to me:

"I was telling Andy the other day what you had found out about managers and executives, the difference between them, that is. Don't think I got it quite straight, though, so why don't you run through it again for the three of us?" He turned to Cranford. "Wouldn't you like to hear it, Gerry?"

Cranford smiled his agreeable smile, and nodded. "Sure," he said, "but I don't mind saying right now that there isn't any difference between managers and executives, so far as I'm concerned; they both have to get things done through people. An executive is just a fancy name for a manager."

"I'm inclined to agree with you, in many respects," Cadmus said, "but I think both you and Andy will be interested in hearing about the differences that a lot of executives apparently see between themselves and managers. How about you, Andy? Want to commit yourself beforehand?"

Resch shook his head. "No, I'd just as soon wait until later. I guess . . ." He hesitated, apparently reconsidering a comment he was about to make, then he continued: "Well, let's see how Mr. Cranford's definition makes out." Resch's deference to Cranford was unforced; he would, I thought, probably continue for a long time to refer to Cranford as "mister" whenever others were present.

I decided to make my explanation of the differences between managers and executives brief, since I was pretty sure Cadmus was only hoping for something that would get the two men into an easy discussion. So I just told them that the executives I'd talked with agreed that there were differences between executives and managers, the clearest one being that executives set the company's policies and managers carry them out. Also, there was general agreement, even among employees, that executives include only "a few at the top" of any corporation.

This last point, I noted, roused the interest of both Cranford and Resch, so I continued talking. I ticked off the five main things that an executive does, according to a "self-portrait" that a *Fortune* survey had developed from those in a position to acquire such knowledge: first, an executive has a direct hand in setting the company's objectives and policies; second, he must make or approve decisions that can seriously affect profits and plans; third, he coordinates several main functions of the company, or of a major division or department; fourth, he maintains and develops an organization of trained subordinates; and fifth, he delegates authority and responsibility, and controls performance through at least one level of supervision.

By the time I finished this run-down Cranford and Resch were listening fairly intently, but I was still convinced that it all sounded to them like a textbook lesson. So I gave them the clincher that almost never fails to get a rise out of those who consider themselves executives. "An executive," I said, "does *all five* of the things I've listed, not just two or three or four. If he doesn't do all five, he's a manager—not an executive—by this definition."

Resch merely nodded at this, in a thoughtful way. Cranford, however, smiled and said, "I don't think that the definition is as strict as it sounds. Seems to me I do all those things, and I never considered myself a top-notch executive." His words sounded modest, and perhaps he really didn't think he was a first-rate executive; but at the same time I doubted that he realized how tough and involved some of these five executive functions actually are.

"Some of these functions sound pretty ordinary," I said. "That job of developing subordinates, for instance, is so familiar and so generally accepted now that I guess any executive who admitted he didn't develop the men under him would be considered mighty odd in most big companies. But I continue to be amazed at the way this job of developing subordinates is passed over by the top men."

"Do you really think so?" Cranford asked. "I'd say that almost every good executive I've known seems to have his eye on some of the bright lads in his company, though he rarely lets them know it. Besides, I'm not sure a boss can do much about training subordinates—directly, that is. Outside of setting an example, or passing along a tip now and then, and a pat on the back occasionally, what in hell is there you *can* do to help a man?"

Resch was watching Cranford with that half-veiled stare of his, and when a waiter passed him something on a tray Resch leaned forward slightly so that his gaze would remain steadily on Cranford. Resch wasn't missing anything that would give him a bearing on his future boss. He was at the beginning of the long process of judging the real intent and sincerity of Cranford against Cranford's words; and to some degree Resch was likely to be doing this as long as he took his orders from Cranford.

I did not reply to the last question, which Cranford had ostensibly put to me, for I saw Resch was getting ready to speak. However, Cadmus cut in before Resch could get his sentence started. Perhaps Cadmus didn't want the two men to get into an argument; at any rate, he changed the subject adroitly with a question of his own.

"Before we get to Gerry's question," Cadmus said, "I'd

like to know what that five-part definition of an executive
means as far as staff men are concerned. I know a lot of
high-ranking men who would be pretty sore if you told
them they were only managers. Take the chief legal counsel
of Amalgamated Iron, for example. Do you think that that
fellow, who earns $85,000 a year plus bonus and stock op-
tions, and who has five well-paid men and a big clerical
staff working under him, doesn't qualify as an executive?
I'm damn sure he thinks he does!"

"Of course he does," Cranford replied, a bit impatiently,
I thought. "And what's more, unless Amalgamated's president is just stupid, I'm sure he intends his chief counsel to
continue considering himself a big-shot executive. Fact is,
a brilliant lawyer is usually pried away from his law firm
by the promise of high pay—with a shot at stock profits and
long-term capital gains—*plus* a high executive title. I've never
yet seen a successful lawyer who didn't seem pretty eager
to run things his way whenever he got the chance, and that's
a good start toward acting like an executive. Maybe it's
their legal training, but they sure aren't backward about
assuming authority."

"Sounds as if you had some unpleasant memories about
corporation lawyers," Cadmus said. "I have a few myself.
But the point I was making is that some staff positions are
acquiring more and more status in big corporations. Legal
counsel is one, no doubt about that. One of my clients now
pays its legal v.p. $10,000 a year more than the manufactur-
ing v.p. gets. The top market-research and product-research
jobs are also getting upgraded fast, but of course they didn't
have the advantage of a professional status to start with."

"Do you think that's good?" Resch suddenly asked. "I
mean upgrading these staff men."

Cadmus glanced sharply at Cranford before answering,
which probably meant that Cranford had some ideas about

staff men that Cadmus was going to be respectful about. "Frankly," he said, "I think it's almost always damn poor management to give top ranking to those who act as advisers and expert specialists. They're apt to get the big head and start ordering line managers around."

Cranford turned from gazing out of the window and shook his head. "That's one of your pet ideas, Phil," he said, "but I don't entirely agree. I think you'll concede that I've had my share of staff experts who got the big head— I'll never forget that controller we had who tried to pose as a long-range planner—but just the same I think there are many times when the man who's expert ought to be given the real authority to run things. It depends on the company's position in the market, the age of its products, and many other factors. Sometimes you need marketing brains giving the top orders, sometimes financial brains, sometimes product-research brains, sometimes personnel brains. Too many companies, in my opinion, hang onto that old idea that only sales and production managers should be the big deciders and order givers."

There was a considerable pause after Cranford finished, and I guess Cadmus was trying to give Resch a chance to speak on what could be a pretty delicate subject, under the circumstances. Resch was, after all, taking a job as a line production manager with Cranford's company, and undoubtedly he was wondering what Cranford's views would mean for him on the job.

If Resch did wonder, he wasn't letting it show; a broad grin stretched across his face, and he leaned casually back in his chair. "I'd be inclined to agree with Mr. Cranford," he said. "At least in theory. The trouble is, whenever you've got a staff expert who's bright enough to know what to do, he doesn't often seem bright enough to know *how* to do it. He's usually wrapped up in his scheme or plan, and he's

uneasy about people. Oh, sure, he may know what the text-
books say about having to 'get along with people,' handle
them, stimulate them, and so forth, but I've found that staff
men usually seem to do what the book says. They're mostly
interested in ideas, in analyzing things. On the other hand, a
line manager, if he's really a manager, is interested in getting
things done through people. He's in the business of giving
orders in ways that will get them carried out effectively—
and that's a damn big order, believe me. Nearly all his problems are wrapped up in one word: people."

Cadmus looked at me and smiled slightly, apparently
amused by the clichés Resch had used about managers and
their problems with people. But Cadmus wanted to make
sure Cranford didn't assume that Resch was as simple as
his last words might have made him sound. "If I didn't
know you, Andy," Cadmus said, "I'd think you were quoting
some book on how to manage, especially that business about
a manager's problems being mainly people. That's what
we've been hearing for years from all the 'human relations'
boys, and it's done a terrible lot of harm, in my opinion. Of
course people *are* problems for managers, but every good
manager knows that doesn't mean a manager always has to
handle people and persuade them with tender loving care.
Tell them how you straightened out those chaps in the
foundry out in Cincinnati, Andy."

But Cranford spoke up before Resch could respond. "Now,
Phil, don't be too hard on the human-relations boys," he
said. "I'm sure Andy actually practices a lot of the things
they recommend, like trying to see things from the other
fellow's viewpoint, appealing to his pride in doing a good
job, and so forth."

"That's right, Mr. Cranford," Resch said. "Only I'd rather
not say that I 'practice' such things. Makes it sound as if I
were just experimenting, or something like that. The way

I manage people, I guess, is simply to treat each person the way I think will get him to do the best job for me. Of course, that's often easier said than done; but in any case I don't attempt that 'golden rule' method of treating others as I would be treated. People are too damned different for that, I'm convinced."

"I could give you an argument on that," Cadmus said, "but I'm not going to, because right now I'd rather hear someone answer that question Gerry threw out a few moments ago—just what *can* an executive do to develop the men under him?"

Resch shook his head. "That's a real tough question, Mr. Cadmus," he said. "It sounds simple, but it's tricky."

"How so?" Cadmus asked.

"I think I know what Andy means," Cranford said. "It's tricky because no executive can actually develop anybody else. A man has to really *want* to get ahead, to get better at his job and smarter about the company. You can't do much more than encourage him and give him some tips."

Resch looked at Cranford quizzically. "I wasn't going to put it quite that way, Mr. Cranford," he said, "though I'll certainly agree a man has to have ambition if he wants to be a manager. When I said this question of developing a man is tricky I meant that it's possible to give answers to it that sound perfectly O.K. and reasonable, but they actually don't mean anything much."

"You going to start an argument over semantics, Andy?" Cadmus asked.

"Not if I can help it," Resch replied. "What I'm trying to say, I guess, is that all these techniques for executive development that we've been using or hearing about—you know, role-playing, lectures, studying case histories, counseling and coaching, special assignments, and all the rest—these things may be all right technically as training devices, but they don't develop executives. Not by a damn sight. They don't even make good managers, though I'll admit they may help some."

"I see you go along with the idea that managers and executives are different breeds of cat," Cranford said.

"Yes, I do," Resch said, "because an executive is still something pretty special, in my judgment. He operates on a very different level than the one a good manager operates on. I'm sure you would agree to that."

I could see that Cranford felt somewhat caught by Resch's words, which were urging him, not very subtly, to abandon the earlier position he had taken on the subject. Cranford at the same time may have sensed that Resch was flattering him, implying he was one of those "pretty special" executives.

"Well, I think I see what you mean, Andy," Cranford said, "but frankly I'm not much interested in these fine distinctions."

"Well, Gerry," Cadmus said, "you may not be, but I am. I want to hear what Andy means by an executive operating on a different level from that on which a manager operates."

"Don't know as I can explain what I mean too clearly," Resch said. "The men I've considered real executives seem to be much more concerned with where the company and its people are going than with how they are actually doing at the moment, which is what we managers fret about. I guess also that executives I admire have higher standards, all around. I mean they're not only ethical in doing business but ethical in their personal conduct in and out of the company."

Cadmus smiled. "You mean they don't steal from the cash register?"

"No—not just that kind of honesty," Resch replied. "They're honest about everything, especially about their own shortcomings. Maybe humility's the word I want."

I saw a chance to make a point I'd been wanting to make

for some time. "Maybe humility is the word you want, Mr. Resch," I said, "but I'll bet it isn't the word that either Mr. Cranford or you, Phil, would choose. In fact, I am almost certain you three gentlemen would not agree on what the word 'humility' means. Mr. Resch, for instance, thinks it means something close to honesty about oneself. Do you agree with him?"

Cadmus snorted. "I might have known you'd get us into a game of semantics."

"Call it a game if you want to," I said. "You can still learn a lot of things from games—chess, for instance. So come on, Phil, what do you mean by the word 'humility'?"

Cadmus laughed a little, and said, "All right, I'll play, but don't you keep score," He thought for a moment, started to speak, then thought some more. "Well," he finally said, "I guess by humility I mean the state of being repentant, of being sorry for something you've done."

Cranford immediately said, "Can't see that at all, Phil. Humility is not something that happens to you as the result of some act or other. It's a permanent state, something you carry along with you like any other quality. Andy's point about humility being related to honesty about oneself is well taken, I think, though I'm sure I wouldn't have connected the word honesty with humility the way he did. To me, humility means mainly having no arrogance or stupid pride about yourself."

"I could ask you now what you meant by 'stupid pride,' and we could start all over again," Cadmus said. He sounded annoyed by Cranford's refutation.

"Personally," Resch said, "I'm grateful to both of you for your explanations. I think I've got a little clearer idea as to what I really mean by honesty about one's shortcomings. But I'm not going into that at this point. I would just like to remind you, though, that I said *maybe* humility was the word I was after. After hearing you two talk about the word, I'm not so sure now."

Both Cranford and Cadmus were getting ready to ask Resch what *he* meant by humility when I cut in with the point I wanted to make. "Mr. Resch has demonstrated exactly what I was hoping he would," I said. "None of you agree on the meaning of a word that describes a familiar human characteristic. And yet each of you has used, and undoubtedly will continue to use, words like this in judging the men who work for you and with you. The conclusion seems obvious to me: it is simply absurd to say that it takes certain specific qualities to make a successful executive or manager."

"Aren't you being a little dogmatic?" Cranford asked. "We've been using an executive-appraisal form in our company that calls for personal, individual judgments on twelve different qualities, from Initiative through Integrity, and I think we've been picking and advancing the best men right along."

"Who did you say was picking the best men?" I asked.

"Well, we have a system," Cranford replied. "That is, an appraisal committee reviews these forms in consultation with each supervisor, who fills out the forms on the men under him. Then I discuss the final appraisals with the committee and approve all promotions above a certain rank. It's not a very original system, I'm afraid."

"From what you say, the system does sound like a good many others," I said. "I'm not doubting that it uncovers the managers you consider to be the best, but I think it's basically *your* system. Since you are the final judge, it's inevitable that your standards would long ago have filtered down the line to affect the opinions and judgments of your subordinates. I'm not saying this is wrong; it's what happens in any company. The point is that it's your individual interpretation of a manager's qualities that sets the yardstick—and it's going to be a different yardstick, in many ways, from the yardsticks used in other companies. So, I repeat, it's absurd to say it takes certain qualities to make a successful executive."

Cranford did not argue the point, only smiled again and said, "I see what you mean, though I think you're giving me too much credit for educating the judgments of my executives."

"If you didn't do that kind of educating, I wouldn't, quite frankly, consider you an executive," I replied.

"Now wait a minute," Cadmus said. "What you're saying is that only the top men's ideas and judgments about men count in a corporation."

"No, I don't think he's saying that," Resch said. "He simply said that the top man's opinions and judgments help determine the opinions and judgments of his subordinates. And I'll testify that that's an everyday fact of life in the corporations I've worked for."

I indicated by a nod that Resch had interpreted me correctly. Cadmus, however, continued to question the point. "Well, then, would you say a subordinate can also help determine his boss's opinions and judgments about people?"

"Of course," I replied, "and especially if he's got the makings of an executive."

Cadmus looked at me and grinned, and I was sure then that he had been debating the point merely to draw Resch out in front of Cranford, and vice versa.

Resch turned to me and asked, "Isn't this matter of qualities always complicated by all the differences between executive jobs, between companies, and between industries? Seems to me you couldn't rightly say that any management quality was essential in all situations."

"Not only that," I replied. "In my observation a particular trait may be important in an executive at one point, and a liability at another time. Aggressive ambition, for instance, can be a real handicap when a man gets into a position where tactful patience is frequently called for."

"You know," Cadmus said, as though he were talking to himself, "it occurs to me that this discussion is leading to some rather controversial conclusions. One of them could be that every human quality is merely a figment of someone's imagination!" Cadmus sounded definitely annoyed. "Seriously," he continued, "if the traits of a good manager mean so many different things at so many different times, why bother with them at all? Isn't it just barely possible that people could agree, in a more or less general way, what they mean by a man with initiative or loyalty or fairness or whatever?"

"That's what I was getting at a while ago," Cranford said, "and I forgot to say that on our executive-appraisal forms we have put down simple, easy-to-understand definitions of every quality, so each manager will know what he's expected to judge."

"That sounds better than letting the managers go it alone," Resch said. "From what's been said, though, this doesn't mean that the traits defined on the form are really those you would find in every good manager."

"You know," Cadmus said, "I could throw a small bomb into all this talk about qualities by quoting what some of the sociologists and 'behavioral science' experts now say about executives."

"Such as what?" Cranford asked.

"Well, one point they keep insisting on is that a manager's performance is determined as much by the company situation he's in, and by his relations with 'the group,' as it is by any qualities he may possess. They talk about things like 'hedonic tone' and 'viscidity.' Then on top of this, executive-development specialists insist that the main thing you have to do is to analyze and classify the executive's job, and then figure out what characteristics are needed for success on that particular job. Many training directors have stopped trying to train men to evaluate a manager's personal traits; they're concentrating on getting them to describe only the way a manager works and responds to 'situations.' All things considered, the old search for executive qualities is considered much too naïve an approach by a lot of people I talk to to-day."

"If I believed all the stuff these social scientists are saying about executives and management," Cranford said, "I doubt if I'd be able to get through one working day. A while ago, 'communications' was the big thing—you had to communicate, make a 'two-way street,' listen to everybody, and so on. Then it's been 'group dynamics' or leadership or motivation or organization or some other damn thing. They're analyzing this management business to death, in my opinion."

"But don't you think they've found out some useful things, Mr. Cranford?" Resch asked.

"Oh, I guess so," Cranford conceded. "What annoys me most, probably, is reading some elaborate description of something every executive ought to know, if he's really any good. Like that idea of listening to your subordinates."

"The trouble is, Gerry," Cadmus said, "you're a good executive, and you therefore know, by instinct, background, experience, or whatever, what to do and how to do it."

"Bet you say that to all your clients, Phil," Cranford said.

"I wish I could," Cadmus replied, "but the fact is that I've got some real problem children on my hands. They have got the titles that make them think of themselves as executives, but they're actually not even good supervisors. What's more, they don't want to learn how to manage—they leave

this to others and usually spend their time on some one angle
of the business, such as financing, in which they're technically competent. I once hoped I'd be able to stir some of these
fellows into improving themselves, but now I'm resigned to
letting retirement or death gradually remove them."

"Guess that's your occupational hazard," Cranford said.

"What about putting a lot of good executives through the
psychological testing and interviewing mill to see what made
them good?" Resch asked. "I read somewhere that this has
been done. Think it was some management-consulting firm."

"That's right. Richardson, Bellows & Henry did a lot of
research on over 600 highly rated executives," Cadmus said,
"and my recollection is that they came up with some interesting stuff. For example I think they found that, generally
speaking, a man who's going to be a good executive shows
his maturity early. If a company follows any such rule, of
course, it's bound to miss some good men who bloom late.
Still, maybe that's the price of getting at least most of the
good managers spotted and usefully assigned at an early
age."

"For my money," Resch said, "the price is too high. I
remember two young managers who worked under me a few
years ago, both awful slow in growing up, but they finally
turned out much better than any others their age in the shop.
One later left and is now president of his own company. The
other one should be getting the top job where he is pretty
soon now. I wouldn't give much for any training system that
would have skipped over these two when they were youngsters."

"I'll go along with Andy on that," Cranford said. "In my
opinion it's worth more to a company to locate and promote
one really outstanding manager than it is to select a platoon
of men who are merely good, and then miss the top man.
Andy, if you can spot and train two more men like those two

chaps you were talking about, I won't ask you for anything more in the way of an executive-development program."

Resch grinned and looked over at Cadmus. "I'll try, Mr. Cranford, but I'll need Mr. Cadmus to give me a hand. It's only his *personal* brains I want to pick, not his professional brains, and the easiest way to explain what I mean by his personal brains is just to say I know he's been around the company quite a while and I'm sure he's collected a lot of information about a lot of people in it. I have a lot of respect for your consultant's judgment. However, I naturally have to respect my own judgment the most when it comes to selecting men who look as if they would be good managers someday. That doesn't mean I won't take advantage of any leads I can pick up from psychological tests and appraisal reports, but I have to run these things through my own computer before I put any real stock in them."

"How is that computer of yours programed?" Cadmus asked. "Must be specially wired for picking future presidents."

"Actually, I guess I'd have to say it's rewired, to some extent, for every job," Resch replied. "I mean I just don't have any standard yardstick to apply to the men I have to appraise. And I don't mind saying I think all the efforts still being made to find a 'yardstick' are silly. Every good manager is different, and every job is not only different, but it can be done right in different ways."

"What you're saying, Andy," Cadmus said, "is that picking good managers is still an art, and will never be a science. I've been hearing that for as long as I can remember, but it hasn't stopped the psychologists and those other behavioral scientists from trying to reduce the techniques of management to a system that can be applied by any halfway intelligent person. And they aren't doing this alone, as you certainly know. You'll find executives everywhere who sincerely believe they're gradually developing a real science of management. If you argue with them, they usually think you're a lobbyist for a lot of old-fashioned, hidebound clients."

Cranford grinned. "Maybe you are, Phil," he said. "Take me. I'm kind of old-fashioned about many things, and our company has belonged to the N.A.M. for years."

"Yes, I know how old-fashioned you think you are," Cadmus said, smiling, "and if the N.A.M. knew what you really thought of its ways, Gerry, it would have to ask for your resignation. I'm not worried about you, or even about those executives who think they're out there pioneering on the frontiers of a new management science. They'll at least learn what they *can't* do as managers. But I *am* worried about all those thousands of managers who seem to be taken in by what I call 'The Holy Most.'"

"How's that?" Cranford asked. He sounded a bit shocked.

"I call it 'The Holy Most' because so many businessmen I know now believe that if they read or hear where such-and-such a management technique is practiced by *most* executives, or some idea or opinion seems to be held by *most* executives, then they right away assume that that technique or opinion or idea is the right one. The approval of the majority, in other words, they consider a sure guide to what's best for everybody."

"The majority opinion doesn't necessarily *have* to be wrong," Cranford said.

"No, it doesn't," Cadmus said, "and that only makes it easier to accept. But when I hear someone say he's adopting some practice, and then he adds that it's what 'most other companies' are doing, I usually find out later that that person's thinking isn't very sharp about a lot of things."

"Of course, you know," Cranford said, "civilization wouldn't have got very far if men hadn't been willing to accept conclusions that other men had drawn from their experiences."

Cadmus looked at me and grinned. "Yes, I know," he said, "and my journalist friend here would be the first to agree that other people's conclusions are useful. But I think that his trade is largely responsible for the worship of 'The Holy Most,' simply because publishers and advertisers are so heavily dependent on majority opinions and on broad generalizations. Those surveys about business techniques and about executives are full of the kind of thing I object to."

"You're right," Resch said, "and since you've mentioned it, I will say, with apologies to your journalist friend, that I consider journalism mainly responsible for the loose thinking that goes on about business management, and especially those surveys on managers and executives. Why should anyone conclude that because, say, 65 per cent of some group of managers think or do such and such, that that's what is the correct or best thing to do?"

"Maybe it's not the journalists, Andy, but the sociologists we should blame," Cadmus said. "Wasn't it sociology students who started the nose-counting business to find out what percentage of a group or race does or thinks this or that? This kind of information can be very useful to politicians and to salesmen or anyone else who wants to persuade people. I think the trouble is that in a democracy the opinion of the majority is so respected it's considered a safe guide in nearly everything."

"Well, it's not safe when it comes to managing people," Resch insisted. "I'd like to have a dollar for every survey of executives I've seen which tries to prove that 'most executives' do or think this, that, or the other thing. And when I check with some of my manager friends, I usually find that, like me, they're not doing what 'most' executives are supposed to be doing. My friends may be odd in many ways,

but they include some of the best managers I've ever known."
Resch turned to me. "Sorry to be so hard on management
surveys," he said.

"You needn't apologize," I replied. "I agree with just about
everything you and Phil said about them. Trying to use a
statistical survey to prove some point about managers and
executives makes no sense." My remark clearly surprised
Resch and Cranford. "I won't try to defend the ordinary use
of surveys by magazines and newspapers," I continued,
"though I'm sure a lot of writers and editors would give you
a strong argument for it. But I will defend the survey *Fortune* published in 1958 on the meanings of executive qualities. That survey publicly disclaimed any intention of being
a scientific poll, and said that the small sample of seventy-
five executives who were questioned was *not* typical or av-
erage in any way, and that their replies had no statistical
significance. Finally, it was specifically pointed out that personality traits which were cited more often by more executives were *not* therefore more significant or 'essential' than
other traits. In other words, we did what we could to warn
readers against drawing false conclusions from the survey.
In fact, the main thing we *did* want readers to grasp was that
executives showed an astounding diversity of opinions on the
subject of executive qualities. For instance, I recall that
these seventy-five executives came up with 147 different
descriptive statements about the trait of 'dependability.'"

"Sounds to me as if that survey must have confused many
of your readers," Cranford said. "If executives are that far
from agreeing on what a single quality means, how can you
expect any of them to agree on what it takes to make a good
manager?"

"That's just the point, Mr. Cranford," Resch said. "No two
executives ever agree exactly on what makes a good manager,

and what's more, in my experience, the better the executive the harder it is to tell what he looks for in a man."

Cadmus shook his head. "The sociologists and psychologists I know wouldn't like that kind of talk, Andy," he said, "any more than they'd approve of that *Fortune* survey on executive qualities. You're practically saying that there are no objective standards for judging a man, only the personal opinions and prejudices of the person doing the judging. I think that's going too far. Wouldn't you concede that a manager can be judged to a large degree by his performance on the job, by his success in achieving objectives?"

"Sure, Mr. Cadmus, I agree his job performance will count a great deal," Resch said. "In fact, I'd say it's the payoff. If he doesn't accomplish his job, he isn't a good manager. But I don't think that's saying much of anything. The big question is, *how* does he get his job done? To answer that one, you've got to be able to size up a lot more in a man than just his efficiency in getting and keeping his department on the ball."

Cadmus turned to Cranford. "I don't seem to be getting my point across about judging job performances, Gerry," he said. "Can you help me out?"

"I don't need to, Phil, because I agree with both you and Andy," Cranford answered. "The performance of a manager on a job has to be measured by concrete results and also by what the manager shows he's got as a person—and what he hasn't got. And of course it's almost always those personal traits and virtues that decide how a manager will do his job."

Cadmus shrugged. "Well, don't say I didn't try to put in a good word for some old-fashioned, easy-to-measure standards of job performance. But now that we're back to personality traits again, I'd like to hear someone tell me how a man can learn to judge those things, especially since they all seem to mean something different to every executive."

"I don't think I could tell anyone how to learn that," Cranford said. "It's too complicated. A man's got certain qualities himself, and he watches others, maybe imitates some he admires, and gradually he gets so he can detect a good man pretty fast. But it's not anything easy or simple."

"I agree with Mr. Cranford," Resch said, "and about the only thing I might add is that a manager can learn a tremendous amount about the traits of a manager by studying his own traits, and the ways he himself handles situations and people. But he'll have to remember that other managers will be different from himself; they won't judge people by the same standards, or be impressed by the same things in a person. I believe the more he can learn about why other managers have different views from his own, the more he'll learn about himself—and that's the big thing, to understand yourself."

"You mean," Cadmus asked, "if an executive thinks one of his men thinks highly of someone he doesn't think much of, and he can find out why, then he'll understand more about his own prejudices?"

"That's right," Resch replied, "only you make it sound too simple, as if anyone could do it after one easy lesson. It's awful hard work. Sometimes I find out I haven't really learned what I thought I'd learned, but have only kidded myself. Even that's helpful, of course. But I think the best thing a manager can develop from his experiences in this process of understanding himself is real discrimination. He learns to recognize his own weaknesses and strengths accurately, and he learns to distinguish between those that make a better—or a poorer—manager and those that simply give him a colorful personality." He thought a moment before continuing. "It just occurred to me that the more discriminating he is about things like personality traits, the more he's going to learn from his experiences."

I saw that Cranford was looking intently at Resch now. "I don't think I ever went about it that consciously," Cranford said. "Still, I guess you've described what I consider the toughest part of being an executive, that is, knowing about yourself, and controlling your reactions, being objective, and so on."

There was a pause, and then Cranford suddenly looked again at his watch. "Sorry to interrupt this interesting discussion, gentlemen," he said, "but it's time I got back and did a little work for the company—and maybe also tried out what I've learned today." He smiled at Resch, who smiled back, and I guess we all knew Cranford was mostly kidding. But not entirely.

Five years later I heard from Cadmus that Resch had followed Cranford up the ladder, moving into Cranford's vice presidency when Cranford became president, and when Cranford suddenly died in a plane crash, Resch was immediately elected to the presidency of General Products. He had, of course, long since favorably impressed every member of General Products' board.

I asked Cadmus if he thought he could ever describe what it was that Resch had that made him so good as an executive. Cadmus was amused by the question. "Sure I can describe it," he said. "It's just those good, tasty old-fashioned virtues decked out in a modern package. Things like initiative, judgment, integrity, courage, stability, fairness, and so forth."

"Come on, Phil," I protested, "you know you haven't said anything yet. What do you mean by these virtues?"

"It's not what I mean, it's what Resch means by them," Cadmus replied. "He's still raising questions about qualities like dependability and integrity, asking himself what such traits mean to him, and asking others for examples of what they mean by these words. Says he keeps finding out more about himself that way, such as what traits he's short on. Maybe what's more important is the way he keeps applying his insights to his daily experiences in the company, and outside, too."

"Sounds like a pretty reflective fellow," I said.

"I'd say discriminating is a better word for a man like Resch," he replied.

The more I've thought of it, the more I am inclined to agree with Cadmus. Increasing discrimination still seems to come closest to explaining, in one word, the performances of the most competent executives and managers I have had the opportunity to observe. But I decided the best way to explain their discrimination was to put down some specific evidence I'd collected on what such men mean by some of those old familiar human traits, the kind that show up so critically in the management world. The results of my effort comprise the remaining chapters of this book.

CHAPTER TWO                    *Good*

                              *Judgment*

*To say that a manager lacks good judgment is very
nearly as damning as to say that he lacks integrity.
Good judgment in an executive appears as a rich
compound of qualities, including, for example,
foresight, decisiveness, discrimination, and that
large residue of practical experience which enables
an executive to avoid bad judgment. These varied
ingredients of judgment are so variously related
that it is difficult to say, for instance, whether an
executive's judgment depends on his foresight, or
vice versa. The recognition of good judgment is no
less difficult, and strictly speaking is confined to
those who have developed this trait themselves.
However, since the results of good judgment are
apparent to all, those who can exhibit this trait do
not remain unnoticed for long.*

*In this chapter, the display of judgment, good
and bad, is presented in the form of some imaginary
memoranda, letters, and telegrams exchanged
among five executives of a corporation. Their correspondence deals with the subject of cost cutting,
and is assumed to have begun when the 1957 recession was beginning to be felt. The fictional*

*board chairman is seldom in the office, but likes
to be kept fully informed, and the correspondence
between him and the president, a much younger
man, is unusually formal and detailed.*

October 15, 1957

Mr. Samuel B. Millwright
856 Fifth Avenue
New York, N.Y.

Dear Mr. Millwright:

This is to express my appreciation for the support you gave
me yesterday at the board meeting. It is always reassuring
to know that one's suggestions have the support of Tharmite
Inc.'s board chairman and his long years of experience in
achieving profitable operations.

Along with all the other reasons why I felt Tharmite
should institute an economy program at this time, there was
one I did not want to go into at yesterday's meeting. I think
that the development of an economy program in Tharmite
will provide me an excellent opportunity for appraising the
managerial talent of Tharmite's key men—Vice President
Wolf, Vice President Thorndike, and Mr. Pease, the Treasurer. Each of these men I consider entirely competent in his
own way, but I have not yet been able to convince myself
which of them has those qualities which might qualify him
for more responsibility, and specifically for the post of executive vice president. As you have known for some time, I have
been desirous of finding a capable executive officer to assist
me directly.

The qualities of judgment and foresight seem to me of the
greatest basic importance for this position, and along with

these I am looking for the kind of *intelligent* decisiveness which can only be exercised after the application of good judgment and foresight. All three qualities will be tested, I believe, in the ways these officers approach Tharmite's economy program. The need for actual cash savings should sharpen their decisions; and a suggestion that we simply reduce all expenses by 10 per cent, as some companies do, won't impress me as an indication of good judgment. I will arrange to communicate my findings to you from time to time.

I hope you and Mrs. Millwright had a comfortable trip back to New York.

Respectfully yours,

R. B. COREY

President

October 16, 1957

TO:     T. L. Thorndike, Vice President, Sales
        M. W. Wolf, Vice President, Manufacturing
        D. Pease, Treasurer

FROM:   R. B. Corey, President

SUBJECT: Program for reducing expenses

Implementing my informal comments to you at our luncheon today, I am convinced that a more concerted effort must be made to effect very substantial reductions in Tharmite's operating overhead. There is no need for me to re-emphasize the point that the recession in business in the last few weeks has made serious inroads into our sales figures, and the consequent decreases in production volume have cut profit margins to the bone. Nor do I need to remind you of that old adage that a dollar saved is a dollar earned.

Therefore I am asking each of you to let me have your specific thoughts and suggestions as to areas in which savings might be effectuated. If we all pull together on this I am sure we can turn in a performance we will all be mutually proud of.

October 17, 1957

TO:        Mr. R. B. Corey, President

FROM:    D. Pease, Treasurer

SUBJECT: Suggestions for reducing expenses

In response to your memorandum of yesterday, with which I am in total agreement, the following suggestions are submitted:

1. Reductions in sales bonuses: Though over-all sales figures are off, these items continue to run into large amounts each month, mainly due to the decision to offer the entire sales force the opportunity of earning extra bonuses on sales of the new Palinode clamps. Elimination of those bonuses would save approximately $2,850 a month.

2. Reductions in salesmen's allowances: The outlays for traveling expenses have increased by nearly 10 per cent since the first of the year, following the inauguration of the policy that permits a salesman to return by air to his home each weekend, if he has been working more than 200 miles from home for more than two weeks. The savings to be anticipated from a suspension of this policy are estimated at approximately $1,450 a month.

3. A reduction in year-end inventories of finished goods could improve our cash position appreciably, which would allow us to save on interest charges. An officer at the First National Bank informs me that if the company reduces its inventory position by $200,000, a new loan for $300,000 could be arranged at 3¾ per cent, which would save us $8,750 in interest charges.

In addition to these suggestions, there are certain other

economies possible in salaries, which the wage and salary review committee is scheduled to consider next week. These matters, of course, are entirely up to the finance committee and yourself.

October 17, 1957

TO: Mr. R. B. Corey

FROM: M. W. Wolf, Vice President, Manufacturing

Re that cost-cutting program, Bob, I've already told you my big idea on this score, and will just jot it down here for the record. I think this is no time to go looking for pennies in savings, and I hope you are not considering postponing those equipment replacement purchases scheduled for next month. In the last analysis, the way to attack this cost problem, I am convinced, is to reduce our manufacturing costs as fast as possible, and the fastest way to do this, I believe, is to buy up the Flexo Mills Co., which has about the lowest operating costs in the industry.

Now I know the executive committee turned this proposition down last April, but I still believe there are really big opportunities in this deal not only for cutting costs but for giving us an exclusive and profitable product in a new market. The executive committee's decision, I am positive, would have been very different if it had acquired all the facts on the Flexo Mills proposition.

In view of this, I wish to put my neck out and offer to investigate and round up all the data on Flexo Mills and present this to the board for its consideration.

NPA83 DL COLLECT = KANSASCITY KANS OCT 18 1045 AMC
R.B. COREY, PRESIDENT =
THARMITE CORP. THARMITE BLDG., TOLEDO OHIO
YOUR MEMO ON REDUCING EXPENSES HANDED ME JUST AS I
LEFT THURSDAY FOR MIDWESTERN SALES GET-TOGETHER.

BEEN TURNING OVER SOME IDEAS EN ROUTE OUT HERE AND
THINK WE SHOULD REDUCE OUR EXPENSE RATIO BY STEPPING
UP OUR EFFORTS IN ADVERTISING AND SELLING. WE CAN AND
SHOULD INCREASE THE USUAL BONUS PRIZES FOR SALES OVER
QUOTAS. BUT THE SALES FORCE NEEDS AN EXTRA PUSH NOW,
AND TIM GATES OF OUR AGENCY TELLS ME HE HAS A REALLY
HARD HITTING SCHEME TO COUNTERACT THE PRESENT LULL
IN SALES INCREASES. HE WANTS TO BRING OUR CUSTOMERS'
FAMILIES RIGHT INTO THE SELLING SITUATION. SOON AS HE
GETS HIS PLAN INTO SHAPE I WILL SUBMIT IN DETAIL TO YOU.
MEANWHILE WISH TO SUGGEST THAT OUR RESEARCH DE-
PARTMENT PUT IN SOME INTENSIVE WORK ON THAT NEW
FLAMEPROOF EXTENSOR. THIS COULD REALLY PUT US OUT IN
FRONT NEXT YEAR. AS TO CUTTING DOWN ON EXPENSES, I
RECOMMEND: 1) REDUCE OUR STOCKS IN LOCAL DISTRIBU-
TORS' HANDS TO ONLY OUR FASTEST-MOVING ITEMS, LEAVING
OUR CENTRAL CHICAGO WAREHOUSE TO HANDLE ALL SLOWER
MOVING ITEMS; 2) TEMPORARILY STOP HIRING NEW SALES
TRAINEES. THERE ARE PROBABLY A LOT OF OTHER PLACES
WHERE WE CAN CUT DOWN, AND WILL DO SOME MORE
MULLING. BEST REGARDS.

TOM THORNDIKE

October 28, 1957

Mr. Samuel B. Millwright
856 Fifth Ave.
New York, N.Y.

Dear Mr. Millwright:

Since my first letters on the matter of Tharmite's cost-reduction program, I have received several suggestions and
recommendations from the officers. I am passing copies of
their proposals along to you together with my comments, in
line with my proposal to assess the managerial competence

of these men in dealing with this matter.

You will note that in recommending savings by reducing salesmen's bonuses and salesmen's allowances, Mr. Pease makes no mention of the possible repercussions these might have on the sales staff; nor did he check up on the sales increases that have been directly attributable to such extras. In my opinion, that's damn poor judgment on his part.

On the other hand, the suggestion by Mr. Pease that year-end inventories of finished goods be cut is an excellent one, in my opinion. I have already advised Mr. Wolf to begin reducing shipments to stock.

Now as to Mr. Wolf's own proposals for the cost-reduction program. In spite of the executive committee's findings last spring, he remains convinced that we should merge with Flexo Mills to get the advantage of their efficient new equipment. I have always had great respect for Marty Wolf's judgment and so am inclined to think it might be advisable to let him undertake the investigation he suggested. Your own views on this would be most helpful.

The point Wolf makes about not postponing the purchase of new equipment is naturally understandable from his viewpoint, but the finance committee has decided so positively against further capital investment at this time that there is no use discussing this matter further.

I am pleased at Tom Thorndike's thinking on two matters —revising the stocking of fast and slow-moving items, and suspending the hiring of new sales trainees. These suggestions make good sense. But the scheme he plans to submit on using our customers' families in promoting Tharmite's products makes me a bit uneasy. We have always left the job of selling strictly to our dealers.

Your comments would be greatly appreciated.

Respectfully yours,<br>R. B. COREY

*Millwright to Corey—Oct. 31*

Dear Bob:

Thank you for your interesting letter on Tharmite's cost-reduction program, and the suggestions of Messrs. Pease, Thorndike, and Wolf.

I'm inclined to state flatly that Mr. Pease's ideas appear to me the most practical and promising, though I was surprised he did not mention cutting down on salesmen's phone calls and telegrams. When I was president, it was taken for granted that the real savings in expenses could be found in the sales and advertising department.

I am frankly surprised that you seem favorably disposed toward Mr. Wolf's proposal that he investigate the purchase of Flexo Mills. I know this firm has a reputation for low manufacturing costs, but the executive committee's case against this merger was entirely conclusive, in my opinion.

The main criticism, you recall, was that Flexo Mills' president was asking for a lifetime retirement contract which the committee thought was too costly for Tharmite; and Flexo Mills' other demand that we absorb all their key executives at their present salaries was estimated to increase our administrative payroll by 40 per cent. It would also give us a lot of headaches as to the status of Flexo Mills men in relation to our own executives. We certainly wouldn't want any of our men playing second fiddle to any Flexo Mills man.

All Tom Thorndike's suggestions sound all right to me, including his new sales scheme. I'm inclined to bet on his "creative judgment," as I think it's now called.

Please keep me posted as to how your appraisal of Tharmite's officers is coming along. I have my own opinions as to who should be executive vice president, but will keep this to myself for a while.

*Wolf to Corey—Nov. 3*

Just to let you know, Bob, that output of the lines has been curtailed nearly 20 per cent for the past week. This ought to get the inventories down in short order.

My own feeling, however, is that this move could turn out to be most unfortunate. If we get a year-end run on some items as we did five years ago, we're going to lose a lot of customer good will.

I am still anxious to explore that Flexo Mills deal, and keep hoping you will decide to give me the go-ahead on this soon.

*Corey to Wolf—Nov. 4*

Glad to hear that you've made such fast progress in cutting down shipments to stock.

Regarding your proposal to investigate Flexo Mills, I have decided you should be authorized to do this. Before you undertake your survey, I want to talk over with you several points that are of special concern to the board. We can do this tomorrow morning at eleven in my office.

*Pease to Corey—Nov. 18*

Your directive that all office telephone expenses should be investigated and curtailed wherever possible resulted within the past two weeks in savings of $65.40. Of this amount $58.10 is the result of a reduction in the length of collect long-distance phone calls from salesmen in the field. They have also begun to send in the new reports that you requested, explaining all overtime phone calls.

First National tells me it is now prepared to issue a loan of $300,000 at the new rate of 3¾ per cent to cover our inventory requirements next year.

*Corey to Pease—Nov. 18*

Confirming my phone conversation today, the new loan from First National should be negotiated by you as soon as possible.

Your report on office savings is acknowledged. I am rather surprised that the total amount saved on long-distance phone calls is as small as it is, though I realize that "every little bit helps."

*Thorndike to Corey—Nov. 19*

JUST SPENT FIVE HOURS WITH TIM GATES WHO IS ALSO OUT HERE ON A TRIP AND HE FINALLY SPELLED OUT FOR ME THAT SALES PROMOTION IDEA HE MENTIONED EARLIER. HERE'S A QUICK RUNDOWN: HE PROPOSES THAT WE OR-GANIZE A PRIZE CONTEST THAT WILL GET THE CHILDREN OF DEALERS AND CUSTOMERS TO HELP THARMITE'S SALESMEN. THE PRIZE WOULD BE A BIG POPULAR DOG LIKE A NEWFOUND-LAND PUPPY, TO BE AWARDED TO EACH LOCAL BOY OR GIRL WHO SUBMITTED THE BEST NAME FOR THE PUPPY IN THE JUDGMENT OF A LOCAL COMMITTEE. GATES SAYS TWO LARGE COMPANIES HAVE USED THIS PRIZE PUPPY PROMOTION IDEA AND ONE COMPANY HAS RUN THE CONTEST TWICE. WHAT'S MORE TIM SAYS A RIG CARMAKER IS NOW THINKING OF RUN-NING A SIMILAR CONTEST AWARDING A PET BURRO TO EACH LOCAL WINNER. I THINK WE COULD PEP UP SUCH A CONTEST BY OFFERING CUSTOMERS A TEN PER CENT PRICE REDUCTION ON ALL ORDERS PLACED DURING THE CONTEST. OFFER WOULD BE ANNOUNCED IN A NIGHT LETTER SENT TO THE HOMES OF FIVE THOUSAND OF OUR BEST CUSTOMERS. GATES THINKS THE DOG PRIZE WILL REALLY PULL IN THE ORDERS WHEN THE CUSTOMERS' KIDS START BEGGING POP TO QUALIFY THEM TO ENTER THE CONTEST BY PLACING AN ORDER. I THINK THIS IS A TERRIFIC IDEA AND HOPE YOU WILL TOO. THE TAG LINE COULD BE "NAME THE DOGGIE" AND WE COULD ALSO REFER

TO THE NEWFOUNDLAND'S POWERFUL JAWS IN OUR ADVER-
TISING COPY, STRESSING THE TIGHT GRIP OF OUR CLAMPS
AND FLANGES. THE CONTEST SHOULD GIVE THE COMPANY A
LOT OF FREE PUBLICITY.

IF THERE IS ANY WORD FROM THE RESEARCH DEPART-
MENT ON DEVELOPMENT OF THAT NEW EXTENSOR IT
WOULD BE MUCH APPRECIATED. COMPETITION OUT HERE
IS GETTING ROUGH.

## Corey to Thorndike—Nov. 20

Your wire was frankly quite a disappointment. Since the
backbone of Tharmite's publicity has always been the trade
journals, a prize contest aimed at the families of dealers and
customers seems wrong. Still, if you and Tim Gates honestly
think this "Name the Doggie" contest would be effective, I
will ask the finance committee to consider it. But let me know
at once how much this program would cost.

In answer to your query about the research on the new extensor, I must advise you that this project has been postponed
in line with the current economy program. The treasurer reported it would be at least three years before Tharmite could
expect to pay off on such an investment. The board voted
that the funds earmarked for such research be applied toward
payment of a small year-end dividend to our stockholders.
Tharmite will need their good will in the lean times looming
ahead.

## Thorndike to Corey—Nov. 21

MANY THANKS FOR YOUR LETTER. SORRY ABOUT THAT RE-
SEARCH PROJECT BECAUSE WE REALLY NEED A NEW ITEM TO
MEET THE COMPETITION. SALES OUT HERE ARE SUDDENLY
STARTING TO PERK UP A BIT, FOR SOME UNACCOUNTABLE
REASON.

RE THAT NAME THE DOGGIE PROGRAM, TOTAL COST OF

THIS PRIZE CONTEST OUGHT NOT TO RUN MUCH OVER
$50,000, INCLUDING PUPPIES, NIGHT LETTERS, NEWSPAPER
ANNOUNCEMENTS OF WINNERS, CONTEST BLANKS, JUDGES'
FEES, ETC. THIS MAY NOT SOUND CHEAP BUT GATES AND I
THINK THE REWARDS COULD BE STARTLING, AND POSSIBLE
TIE-INS WITH OUR FUTURE AD COPY VERY DESIRABLE. HOPE
YOU AGREE.

### *Corey to Thorndike—Nov. 21*

PUT THOSE NEWFOUNDLANDS BACK IN THE DOGHOUSE. YOU
CAN STAY OUT YOURSELF BY REMEMBERING OUR ECONOMY
PROGRAM. ASSUME YOU KNOW LETTERS COST LESS THAN
TELEGRAMS.

### *Wolf to Corey—Nov. 25*

Want to let you know at once, Bob, that things look very
promising on the Flexo Mills deal. The executive vice president gave me an hour this afternoon, and several items got
cleared up.

I found out that our executive committee's main objection
to the merger was the compensation contract that Flexo
Mills' bullheaded old President Ashbaugh insisted on for
himself. He wanted a deferred pay scheme that would have
given him $50,000 a year, tax prepaid, for five years after his
retirement, and I can understand why our directors choked
on this and turned down the merger. But apparently no one
suggested that someone from Tharmite dicker with Ashbaugh. The executive v.p. told me that Ashbaugh fully expected Tharmite to bargain with him for a more modest
settlement. I was given to understand that if Tharmite
agreed to something like $35,000 for five years, and without
the prepaid tax feature, Ashbaugh would probably accept.

Even this looks rather high, but not when you realize that

Ashbaugh's already in his late seventies. On a hunch, I took the precaution of checking up on his family's mortality rate and found that none of his parents or grandparents lived to be over eighty, and an insurance man tells me that the actuarial averages are heavily against him.

The problem of having Tharmite take over Flexo Mills' key men in case of a merger is also, I discovered, not so troublesome as it looks. The executive v.p. told me he has talked with most of the top men and only two men, he said, were planning to join Tharmite if the merger went through. However, in my judgment it would be a mighty good thing if we held onto some of Flexo Mills' younger men.

This information, I believe, should be sufficient to convince the board it ought to reconsider the Flexo Mills proposition.

P.S. A last minute bit of news from the shop: I just learned that the warehouse has unexpectedly started to back-order six sizes of flange bodies. Replacement of this stock from our shop was delayed by a supplier's shortage of flanges, and emergency replacement has been ordered from another source. But overtime and other extras on this rush order may cost us a good bit of money, maybe $7,000 over the regular price. I've been afraid right along that that across-the-board cutting down on inventory replacements would bite us.

*Corey to Wolf—Nov. 25*

Your report on Flexo Mills really makes me feel good, Marty. I rather thought the executive committee hadn't explored that merger business carefully enough. I am taking it up with the board early in December. Many thanks for a bang-up job.

About those stock shortages of flange bodies: Better get that rush order in extra fast. You know how much these items can mean to our best customers, especially sizes 4-A and 6-B.

*Wolf to Corey—No. 26*

Sorry, Bob, but that rush order from the new flange supplier has been stymied by a truckers' strike. Am trying to get
replacements from another source. Sales department just
phoned that Universal Swivel Inc. is yelling for two gross of
model 4-A. Thorndike is being advised of situation.

*Thorndike to Wolf—Nov. 27*

CAN'T SOMETHING SPECIAL BE DONE IMMEDIATELY TO GET
OUT THOSE MODEL 4-A FLANGE BODIES FOR UNIVERSAL
SWIVEL? HOW IN HELL DID WE RUN SHORT OF THESE ANY-
WAY? PLEASE ADVISE SOONEST. AT BEVERLY HILLS HOTEL.

*Wolf to Thorndike—Nov. 27*

SORRY CANNOT PROMISE ANYTHING RE STOCK ON 4-A
MODELS. TRUCKERS' STRIKE AND INEXPERIENCED NEW SUP-
PLIER CAUSING DELAY. SHORTAGES APPARENTLY CAUSED BY
RECENT BAD ESTIMATES PLUS POLICY ON INVENTORY REDUC-
TIONS. LET ME KNOW IF YOU HAVE A BETTER EXPLANATION.

*Thorndike to Corey—Nov. 29*

On my return to New York this afternoon I found the unfortunate shortage of 4-A flange bodies, which still looks very
grim, for Marty Wolf says he can't get the new supplier to
deliver before December 10. Universal Swivel's vice president phoned me this morning he would have to find another
source if we couldn't promise delivery by December 6.

In view of the urgency of this shortage, would it not be
advisable to ship out to Universal Swivel some of those new
experimental 4-aaa models being made for the testing labs?
To keep a good customer is worth a big risk. If the experimental models really don't pan out, I feel sure I can smooth
things out with Universal Swivel.

Those inventory cuts may have been a good idea for the

financiers, but it looks to me like a case of damn poor judgment.

## Corey to Thorndike—Dec. 2

Your suggestion that the trouble with Universal Swivel over the shortage of 4-A models at this time can be alleviated by shipping them some experimental 4-aaa models is acknowledged. I think some more thought on this matter would be advisable. I see two big objections: (1) if the models failed at Universal Swivel, we would lose not only a good customer but also our reputation for superior, pre-tested merchandise; (2) our own shop is already working overtime to get out the mounts for the 4-A flanges, which means a very expensive increase in inventory if they aren't shipped out before year end. Weighing these two factors against the possible loss of Universal Swivel's business, I am inclined to risk the latter. I have great confidence in your ability to keep that customer happy with Tharmite.

## Wolf to Corey—Dec. 3

It has just been brought to my attention that approval of the purchase of new sports equipment has not yet been received from your office. Since the union is anxious for the employees to get this equipment, would it be possible for this matter to be cleared before our labor-management committee meets at the end of this week?

## Corey to Wolf—Dec. 4

I sincerely regret to have to inform you that the executive committee has eliminated the tentative appropriation for the sports equipment project. It was felt that its cost, estimated at $750, could not be justified in the light of our present efforts to minimize all expenditures not essentially required.

*Wolf to Corey—Dec. 4*

I got pretty mad this afternoon when I got your memo, Bob, but have cooled down enough to get something off my chest. It never seems to dawn on the executive committee that the workers of this plant are the most important machinery we've got, and if we don't keep their morale up we might as well forget all about production efficiency.

Now I know baseball gloves and balls, etc., aren't going to make a great big happy family out of the employees. The point is that too many of them already think that the big boss, which is you, doesn't give a damn about them. We've made time studies, Bob, and it is pretty clear that the men on the line, who are big baseball enthusiasts, can—and do—slow down the line whenever they even think they've got a grievance.

Still you tell me the committee thinks this sports equipment is "expendable." Hell, Bob, sometimes I get to thinking maybe I'm the one who is expendable.

*Corey to Wolf—Dec. 5*

Your opinions on the sports equipment matter are appreciated, Marty, and have stimulated me to give it some further thought. My conclusions still are that the committee was right in eliminating this from the budget, and that you are wrong. But my reasons are not the same ones I had at first. Now I think you and I might spend some time discussing this whole business. How about Friday morning at nine-thirty?

*Corey to Millwright—Dec. 10*

This is to bring you up to date on Tharmite's economy program and, in connection with this, my own appraisal program on Messrs. Wolf, Thorndike, and Pease.

Since my last communication on these matters, I have

been doing some homework. I've done a good deal of reading on the subject of executive "decision-making" and anything else I could find that seemed to analyze these qualities of judgment and foresight. I have talked to a good many friends in other firms, and also have been in touch with Professor Hageborn of my university's Business School. I'm afraid that Tharmite's executives, myself included, still have a lot to learn.

One thing I found out is that no two executives are likely to agree on exactly what they mean by these or any other managerial qualities. Professor Hageborn wrote me that he had amused himself for a long time by jotting down the various descriptions of business judgment which executives themselves used in some of those courses where management people come back to the campus for several weeks. He had collected nearly a hundred different verbs utilized in this connection, and had sorted them into six groups. I thought you might be interested in samples from his list:

1. Evaluate, judge, weigh, sift, deliberate, etc., etc.
2. Think, reason, analyze, interpret, relate, etc., etc.
3. Consider, perceive, grasp, identify, etc., etc.
4. Decide, reach conclusion, rule out, find solution, etc., etc.
5. Foresee, recommend, see around, await timing, etc., etc.
6. Act, merge, focus, use, avoid, inform, alter, smoke out, etc.

It makes me wonder if there is any limit to the things that may be expected of an executive who is to be credited with having "good judgment." In any case, in attempting to evaluate this quality in Tharmite's executives, it seems to me that their recent actions with reference to the program of cost reduction are sufficiently revealing for at least a preliminary assessment.

In my present view, the treasurer, Mr. Pease, has shown

the kind of unimaginative practical judgment that seems to be typical of financial men. His suggestions about cost reduction were orthodox, and reasonable insofar as it is always true that with a little effort money can be saved in salesmen's allowances, bonuses, phone calls, etc. We have actually saved a nice sum by dropping the allowances for salesmen to fly home every weekend. But Pease's suggestions regarding the elimination of the salesmen's bonuses on the new Palinode clamps seemed silly to me, and I vetoed it, since the bonus is a real incentive to the men, and the more clamps they sell the longer we keep our production lines above breakeven.

Pease's recommendation on cutting down on inventory is going to save us money on interest charges, all right; but the special rush orders to fill shortages partly caused by inventory cuts are costing us nearly all the money we'll save in interest charges. Pease's foresight here was pretty weak.

It may finally turn out that Pease's best money-saving suggestion was that review of salary raises for supervisory and management personnel. The finance committee has just taken this up, and we are finding that Tharmite has been carrying too many managers' jobs that don't earn their keep. Some pruning here would produce surprising savings, but Pease can only be credited with an intelligent guess, since of course he didn't have the facts on the relative job performances that would enable him to decide whether or where such economies could be made.

Next there is Tom Thorndike, our sales vice president. Though two of Tom's proposals for cost reduction made good sense, I regret to say that his recommendation that Tharmite start a "Name the Doggie" contest to promote sales revealed a shocking lack of knowledge about marketing experiences with such contests. Fortunately I checked with my friend Bill Stevens, an old hand in the ad business, and learned how dismally similar contests with animal prizes had turned out. The children undoubtedly love the animals, but there is always the risk that some of the animals will cause trouble by biting or stepping on an overeager child. Furthermore Stevens tells me that the parents are often insistent that their children take no part in the contest; dealers report that mothers usually came up and begged them not to let their children sign a contest blank, since the mothers obviously didn't want the bother of feeding and caring for a large house pet.

Tom's idea about sending a weekend wire to our best customers announcing the contest is just as poorly conceived. One company that did this developed a great deal of ill will when Western Union delivered the wires early Sunday morning and woke up a great many good customers.

In addition, Tom's foresight and judgment both deserted him when he proposed that Tharmite ship some new experimental models to satisfy a good customer who was complaining about a recent shortage of our 4-A flange bodies. Thorndike's exhibition of executive ability in these matters was so very poor that I am now very surprised he hasn't tripped up before this. My own judgment probably is to blame here. Since the end of the war, sales have, until recently, gone so steadily in one direction that I may have overlooked a lot of things.

Now I'm planning to keep a very close watch on Tom, and hope I can coach him to be more deliberate and analytical about his decisions. And if that Flexo Mills merger goes through as scheduled, I think a smart newcomer will be sharing some of Tom's executive duties in sales, and that should teach him to do more deliberating and planning.

Finally there is Marty Wolf, our manufacturing vice president, whose one and only recommendation, you will recall, was to re-investigate and complete that merger with Flexo

46 The Men from the Boys

Mills. I know you, Mr. Millwright, opposed a re-investiga-
tion, and I am only now confessing to you that I gave Marty
the go-ahead on this. In my own judgment—and I can't say
exactly why—I thought it was a good gamble to trust Marty's
judgment on this, even though the executive committee had
turned the proposition down. So he re-investigated, and I am
pleased, of course, to report that he has in my opinion dug
up enough information to justify Tharmite's taking over
Flexo Mills.

This whole matter I will have Marty present at the board
meeting next week, but here I want to say that Marty certainly showed good judgment, and foresight and decisiveness, too, in his pursuit of this matter. He got a lot of facts
the executive committee never thought of; he found out, for
example, what kind of specific deal Ashbaugh really would
accept. Marty also analyzed the situation regarding the future plans of Flexo Mills executives, considered the advantages and disadvantages from our viewpoint, and concluded
that a merger would benefit Tharmite over the long term by
reducing all its costs.

Marty is my first choice as of now, but I plan to keep
checking on him and coaching him. He didn't show too much
foresight and judgment when he insisted that we should
never have canceled the appropriation for sports equipment
for the plant employees. This was a small matter in one way,
since there was only $750 involved, but it brings up a larger
point. Marty still inclines to rely on the old-time paternalistic
approach to factory personnel. If this equipment had been
given to Marty's men, in spite of everybody knowing we
were trying to cut down on "frills," it would simply have
been encouraging Marty to continue his paternalistic attitudes. I had a long chat with Marty afterward and I think I
got my points across to the effect that though the paternalistic approach might solve things temporarily, he really needs

to study some of the recent findings about ways to improve employee morale by developing better supervisors down on the line.

That's about the picture as I see it, so far as these three executives are concerned at the moment. Your own comments on this matter would be greatly appreciated. Needless to say, I am anxious to learn whether my choice corresponds with the one which, as you indicated to me, you had made some time ago.

December 12, 1957

Mr. R. B. Corey, President
Tharmite Corporation
Tharmite Building
Toledo, Ohio

Dear Bob:

I hasten to acknowledge your most interesting letter about the executive qualities of Mr. Pease, Mr. Thorndike, and Mr. Wolf. Quite frankly, your selection of Mr. Wolf as the most capable candidate for the executive vice presidency was a very big surprise. I don't think I would have seriously considered him for this job.

Now you in turn may be surprised at my own choice, which is Mr. Pease. I won't bother you with any elaborate reasons for my preference, except to say that he exhibited in my opinion the kind of practical, hardheaded figure sense I would consider essential in an executive vice president. My idea of such an executive, of course, may be quite different from yours, for I never really thought I needed an executive assistant, and if I had had one he would have been largely confined to the kind of thinking about management that Mr. Pease seems well equipped to furnish.

Since you evidently are expecting more of your executive

v.p. than this, I can understand why you have put so much
stress on your appraisal of the judgment shown by these
three men. But personally I still am skeptical about anyone
being able to check up on anyone else's judgment beforehand. I agree with a friend of mine who has been very successful as an executive, who recalled the other day that when
someone asked him how he had developed good judgment,
he replied, "experience." When he was then asked how he
gained experience, he answered, "bad judgment." Good
judgment is certainly a matter of trial and error, and after a
while you get a sense of it. But I can't really explain it.

Also I find it is nearly impossible for me to distinguish between these three qualities of judgment, foresight, and decisiveness. They're all wrapped up together, it seems, yet
they are not identical. A man can have pretty good judgment,
I've found, and still be unable to make decisions—though I
guess most of the executives I know would insist that if you
can't come to form a conclusion to do something (or not do
something) you haven't shown judgment. The way foresight
fits into this is hard to describe, too. One of my friends says
"foresight is the basis of judgment." But you have to have a
lot of good judgment, I think, before you can show any really
good foresight.

This leads me to make a confession I have never made to
anyone except my wife. I know now that I was wrong, but
when the board asked me to name a successor ten years ago
I didn't propose you. I suggested that Tharmite look outside
for a president. And when a committee of the board eventually decided that you should be tendered the presidency, I
was the only one who voted against it. I'll admit now I didn't
show good judgment about you, and in fact based my opinion chiefly on the arbitrary conviction that a man as young
as you were then just couldn't run Tharmite.

Well, I am glad to say that the board overruled me. One

thing this taught me is that the man who continually refuses to trust anyone's judgment or foresight but his own is likely to find out later that he's been very decisive and totally wrong.

Cordially yours,

SAMUEL B. MILLWRIGHT

CHAPTER THREE     *Cooperation*

*Recent gospels of human relations, and the emphasis on "participation" and "group dynamics" in management have put a premium on the cooperative man—or on conformity, as some would have it. The quality of cooperation in an executive might seem one of the easiest to identify; it is, for many reasons, often one of the most difficult. In this chapter, the ramifications of cooperation are jointly explored in a series of memoranda between management consultant Phil Cadmus and his junior partner, Tom Beekman.*

TO: Tom Beekman     (*Confidential*)
    Hotel Brunswick
    Lancaster, Pa.

RE: Conference problems at Plaston Corp.

This is simply a brief follow-up on our conversation at lunch today about your upcoming investigation of the roiling and unhappiness at our client Plaston's Lancaster plant.

The difficulty appears to be real, though I think Plaston's president, Bob Hegeman, is somewhat overexcited about it. He got a large dose of that "participation" training up at Bethel last year, and has gone a little overboard on this business of "interpersonal skills." However, you can expect to find plenty of friction at that plant. There are a good many stiff-necked oldtimers down there who aren't taking kindly to Hegeman's present pressure for "cooperation." I suggest you poke around the plant for a day or so to see what you can pick up on the general situation, before you start digging into the immediate sore spots.

Since this is your first go at a problem of this kind, Tom, I'm also suggesting you send me a short daily report on your findings, and I will try to help from this end with any comments or information that seem useful on this assignment. Incidentally, it might not be a bad idea for you to brush up quickly on the subjects of participation, conferences, group work, etc., for Hegeman is sure to ask a lot of "technical" questions—i.e., he'll want to know about things like "viscidity," "hedonic tone," etc. But don't let these technicalities worry you. As you know, I'm counting on your sharp eyes and good judgment to uncover the source of Plaston's current trouble. We can discuss solutions later. Good luck.

PHIL CADMUS

TO:     Mr. Philip Cadmus
        Executive Studies Inc.
        729 Fifth Avenue
        New York, N.Y.

FROM: Tom Beekman

Well, here's my first report on the Plaston problem. I had a time shaking myself free from Mr. Peebles, the plant manager, who welcomed me in his office this morning and gently insisted on showing me around the place. Could have expected this, I guess, and I'm not regretting it, for it gave me a good chance to watch and talk with Peebles. He is a real nice guy, a bushy-haired, easy-going man who obviously knows production down to the ground. As we walked through the different departments this morning he kept picking up a piece here and a part there and showing me some technical point about it. Noticed he almost always tossed the credit for these things to one or two men in each department, and they seemed to appreciate it. But being with him naturally made my trip a pretty formal one; I could see men and women workers looking at me coldly as though they suspected I was going to be installed as a new manager over them. And when Peebles introduced me as a "consulting engineer," they grew more suspicious, of course; thought I was there to make a time study.

The plant seems very well kept, and I complimented Peebles on having the aisles so well marked, and the machinery well protected. He told me he was "an old Navy man" and always liked having things "shipshape," but when I asked him if he also believed in running "a taut ship," he said that was "nonsense." (If you don't care for all these quotes, please let me know; I realize they can be annoying, but thought they might help give you a clearer picture.) Back in Peebles' office after the plant tour, we talked about morale in the plant (which seems damned good to me, now) and he said he considered good morale an easy thing to secure. His prescription: "Just be friendly and helpful to the boys down the line, show some real interest in them, and keep your promises." When I asked what he thought of the cooperation between managers in the plant, he grunted and said he thought "there was room for improvement," and then he mentioned that there were "a couple of empire builders that needed watching." I didn't ask him for names; thought my project would sit better with him if I generally followed his example and took it easy with such things.

Peebles took me to lunch at a small fish house here on Main Street where a lot of the plant supervisors regularly eat. He was repeatedly hailed by others as we walked to our table, but with great respect. I noticed most everyone called him "Mr. Peebles," and the man who called him "Dan" turned out to be the traffic manager, Cyrus Fargo, a bull-necked, ruddy-faced fellow in his fifties, I'd say. Fargo and Peebles play golf together a lot, Peebles told me, and on his way out later Fargo stopped a moment at our table and kidded Peebles about his golf game; he was plainly curious about me, and suspicious, after Peebles identified me and said, with a laugh, that I ought to take "a real good look at Fargo's department." Fargo didn't laugh, and I expect he would be apt to get pretty touchy in any conference.

While walking back to the plant with Peebles, I noticed a big white Lincoln swoop past us into the driveway, and the driver waved at Peebles, who said to me, "There's our Boy Wonder, Al Cunningham." I gathered that Cunningham, the district sales chief who you told me was racking up such a sales record down here, was no great buddy of Peebles. I tried to see him this afternoon, but no luck; he was rushing off to Philly, so I spent some time with his assistant, William Gately, who is an eager beaver, I think. He made a number of phone calls to department heads while I was with him, briskly checking up on one thing or another for Cunningham, in preparation for a conference Cunningham is calling to-morrow at 11:09 A.M. That's right, 11:09—Gately says Cunningham usually sets conferences at times like 9:32 or 4:53, just to keep others conscious of the starting time and the need for keeping on schedule. Sounds like a fancy *Adprac* to me, for which Gately might be responsible; he's a product of Carnegie Tech's business school, a big, blond crewcut with a quick tongue. He asked me at one point how much the top man in our firm made; and was surprised I didn't know this. He thinks we ought to cut ourselves into some nice option deals through our clients! I am going to be seeing much more of him, I have no doubt.

That's about it for tonight. This town is nice and quiet, and this hotel offered shoo-fly pie for dinner, which I took, to bolster me for an evening of reading about group dynamics. Best regards.

                                                    Tom Beekman

to: Tom Beekman

Your first report was very satisfactory, Tom, and I think you got a good running start on those who are probably most involved with the company's conference difficulties. Keep up the good work, and especially those quotes of the participants you are including; they help me get the feel of things. Speaking of participants, I trust you are enjoying both the shoo-fly pie and your nighttime reading about "participation." I think you are going to find at least some of this material useful at Plaston.

Suggest you take extremely careful observations on Cunningham in this investigation. He may be flashy but he's plenty smart in merchandising, from all I hear, and could be plenty smart in managing his way around others there. You'll know more about everybody, of course, after you've covered that conference Cunningham called for 11:09 this morning. That exact-time gimmick is old, you know, but sometimes it really gets meetings going on time, a kind of slow, preliminary pressure. However, Cunningham may only be using it to impress others with his tight schedule.

Peebles and Fargo seem entirely harmless to me, but you never know. Gately, on the other hand, may be a pony of another feather. Will be looking forward to your next installment. Regards.

PHIL CADMUS

TO:   Mr. Philip Cadmus

FROM: Tom Beekman

Your comments on my last report are much appreciated, and I will welcome any further suggestions you may have about the men down here. Your advice to keep a close eye on Cunningham was certainly dead right as I discovered this morning as soon as he opened his conference. But before I get to him, let me cover a few items I think may be significant.

First, the meeting was held in a good-sized room near Plant Manager Peebles' office; the room was quiet and air-conditioned, the chairs comfortable, and there was a long table in the center which I noted was entirely bare except for ash trays—no pencils, pads, or other items to distract the participants. A visual-aid projector stood in the corner, but was not used. Cunningham apparently was keeping his pitch low. When I arrived with Peebles about five after eleven, we were politely greeted by Bill Gately, Cunningham's assistant; Gately tried to make me feel at home; asked somewhat abruptly if I wanted some pencils or paper, etc., but he was smoothness itself in asking Peebles if there was anything he could get for him before the meeting. When Peebles said no, Gately quickly introduced me to a thin somber-faced chap sitting at the table. This was Nicholas Poglia, manager of the Accounting Department, who just nodded at me and went on studying a sheet of figures he held in his hand. Then Cyrus Fargo, the burly traffic manager, showed up and hailed me before Gately could get his introduction started. Fargo was in high spirits about some golfing joke he'd picked up and wanted to pass it on to Peebles immediately; Peebles willingly gave his ear, and I was about to start some small talk with Gately when Cunningham entered the room, and Gately, the alert beaver, bounded over to his side to ask him something. Cunningham told Gately to "skip it," and then greeted each one of the others individually and with real warmth, I thought. ("Hi, Dan"; "What's with you, Nick?"; and "Glad you could make it, Cy.") He had spotted me instantly, I noted, but didn't let this stop him from observing the amenities with his colleagues. Soon as Cunningham had finished these, he smiled at me, came over and introduced himself; he made no allusion to the fact that none of the others had bothered to introduce me to him—a nice consideration, I thought.

Cunningham is physically impressive, too. He weighs perhaps 200, stands over six feet, and has an open boyish face that seems perpetually cheerful; however, his eyes move so extremely quickly, usually from face to face of those present, that he seems to be watching for adverse reactions every instant, a point that I believe can scarcely escape his colleagues. He plainly considers a conference a selling venture, and he opened this one right on time in a brisk, jovial manner. "I appreciate your all coming here," he said, and then pitched right into his new proposal. His scheme, in a nutshell, is that Plaston should rapidly expand its market for a new plastic panel by making it in several additional sizes; this, he immediately pointed out, would probably mean changes in production layout, in output quotas, and distribution. He closed by asking for their reactions and "especially your advice on the best ways we can get this market-spreader rolling." He then turned to Peebles and said he realized this plan "might bring you some headaches, but

I know you can swing it." And to Fargo he tossed the compliment that the Traffic Department has "a built-in capacity for doing the impossible."

I was watching Peebles and Fargo, expecting one of them would speak up, but I suddenly heard accountant Poglia cut in with his slightly nasal voice: "Yeah, Fargo is good on the impossible, all right, like those fancy costs he ran up last month on the Travers job." There was a silence, and I saw Fargo heating up fast; Cunningham said, "Now, Nick . . ." but got no further before Fargo had reached his boiling point and exploded with: "Aw, you damned pencil pushers give me a pain. That Travers job may have cost money, but it made the company more money than your paper-shuffling department could in a year of Sundays!" Poglia smiled smugly, feigned indifference, and said to Cunningham he was "sorry to have mentioned a little thing like money." This produced some smiles from everybody but Fargo. (It was a direct reference, I learned later, to the recent cost-cutting program, which President Hegeman has been pushing hard.) Fargo just glared and drummed his fingers on the table. Cunningham tried to ease things by asking Peebles for his "comments," but Peebles only said he'd "have to know more about the deal before I could comment." That apparently moved Gately to defend his boss, Cunningham, for he asked "What more is there to know?" Not a very bright remark, of course, in view of the fact that Peebles undoubtedly knows more about the plant than anyone. Gately then made matters much worse by saying to Poglia, "And let's try to keep on the beam, Nick." I could almost see Poglia snarl and spit as he replied, "Look who's talking!" By now Cunningham apparently saw there was no time to lose, and he curtly asked Gately to go out and bring him some sales and shipment figures he'd left on his desk. To my surprise, Gately seemed pleased and at once jumped up and left the room. That seemed to quiet things for a time, and Cunningham helped further by kidding himself, referring to "my early Boy Scout training of being prepared."

While Gately was gone, Cunningham launched into a story about the way the new plastic panel was being snapped up by furniture manufacturers in the Southwest, and he asked Poglia how sales were standing up in other areas. Poglia seemed momentarily pleased by this attention, and pulled out a card he had in his pocket, apparently a recent summary of sales and profit margins by district. As he read off a few figures, Cunningham listened earnestly, thereby further enhancing Poglia's sense of self-importance. Peebles and Fargo listened, too, but not so carefully, and a couple of times, when Fargo whispered something to Peebles while Poglia was reading off figures, Poglia shot him a venomous glance. Then Gately returned with the papers Cunningham had sent him for; but instead of reading off figures from these, Cunningham simply laid the sheets on the table, face down, and said to Peebles, "Before I get into any statistics, Dan, I wish you'd give me the benefit of your honest opinion about producing these new-sized panels. Are they harder to make, or what?" Peebles grinned and replied, "I think your scheme might work, Al, if you'd just let me know how I can increase the output of those damned old machines we've got running these panels now." That drew smiles from everyone (later I learned that it's an old story in the plant that President Hegeman is always pressing Peebles for "more output per machine," even though Peebles has to struggle just to keep some of this antiquated machinery in operation).

The conference still appeared to be stalled, and Poglia now let fly with another dart, this time at Peebles, by asking if Peebles "had found a way to increase the output per man." Peebles didn't flare at all; just looked a little tired and snorted, mildly. But Fargo's temperature rose visibly at this attack on his friend Peebles, and he snapped at Poglia: "Have you ever found anything good to say about anything? You accountants think you're smart when you spend $1 to find 4 cents worth of mistake!" The hardness in Fargo's tone suggested he had been battling the accounting department a long time, and wasn't going to stop. Poglia appeared a little defensive, smiled weakly and repeated his remark about "sorry to have mentioned a little thing like money," but this time no one else smiled.

Cunningham now jumped to his feet and quickly liquidated the meeting, which he obviously thought was not going to get anywhere, at least today. He was smart; he took the blame himself, said he realized he'd "overlooked some points about this plan," and thanked Peebles, Fargo, and Poglia for "helping me see this," and promised to "take some things up with the Old Man" before he called the next meeting, which he explicitly set for a week from today. As the others slowly rose to their feet, Cunningham flatly said, "I will definitely declare this conference null and void." It wasn't really funny, but the others laughed at it, and even Fargo seemed to get rid of the rest of his pique by calling back over his shoulder, "You can say that again, you old huckster!" Cunningham grinned at him and then took Poglia's arm on the way out of the room and began talking quietly to him; from the snatches I could hear as I walked behind them with Gately, Cunningham was earnestly asking Poglia's advice about some financial matter, and Poglia was unmistakably responding in a pleasant way. I asked Gately if he thought Cunningham's plan would go over at the next conference, and first he merely shrugged, then he quickly said he thought his boss "could sell anything."

That winds up my data on conference No. 1. At this point I'll make a guess that Cunningham *does* sell his plan at next week's conference; I think he's got the touch to bring the others along. But I won't bet on it before I've seen Poglia. Am scheduled to talk with him tomorrow. This afternoon I spent mostly with Fargo, on whom I'll file a report later. Regards.

Tom Beekman

TO: Tom Beekman

I found your scenario on that first conference absorbing, and think you have uncovered some of the real sore spots in the plant's cooperation network. But I can't go along with you on that guess that Cunningham will put his plan across at the next meeting. One reason is that there are some important factors working against Cunningham, which I don't think you've allowed for; for instance, there's the fact that the president, Bob Hegeman, is an ex-treasurer who is very cost-conscious and figure-minded—which of course is what Poglia was referring to in his cracks about "mentioning money," and is chiefly what gives Poglia the nerve to behave as he did. Cunningham seems to recognize the importance of winning Poglia over, judging from the attention he gave him after the conference. But this will take some doing.

In addition, there are half a dozen or more other negative points evident from your report. Cunningham hasn't got young Gately under control, or properly trained, as yet (witness Gately's stupid remarks to Peebles and Poglia). Though Cunningham, I noted, had the very good sense to send Gately out of the room on that errand just after Gately had bungled things. Incidentally, Gately seems to be one of the type that thrives on administrative details, setting up meetings, making notations, etc., etc. You'll find plenty of these busy boys around these days, straining to impress their superiors—a common variety of what I call the "Organization Manikin." They're often pretty anxious about themselves, and uncertain; notice how Gately answered your parting question to him—first shrugged, then mouthed confidence in his boss. If he grows brighter, he'll hide his indecision and simply mouth completely orthodox statements. I repeat, the most distressing thing about this as far as Plaston's cooperation program is concerned is that Cunningham doesn't appear to have educated Gately much in the years he's been his assistant.

On the credit side are Cunningham's brisk pace as chairman, his geniality and warmth, and his skill in taking the blame for the conference's failure. He also showed his intelligence in some little details like omitting pads and pencils, and keeping the conference uncluttered. His basic problem, I think, is that he doesn't know the other men really well, and hasn't apparently made much effort to acquaint himself with them and their interests. For instance, he should have known better than to wait until the conference to ask Peebles point blank about the problem of producing those new panels. If he'd dropped around to ask Peebles about this beforehand, and explain his idea, chances are he might have had Peebles' support, or have discovered some way to interest Peebles in his idea—perhaps by getting his advice on sizes, shapes, colors, etc., that might be possible. And Cunningham seems to have made the same mistake with traffic manager Fargo—at least Fargo appeared definitely uninterested in what was being presented. If neither Peebles nor Fargo is ready to play on Cunningham's team, the fault is mainly Cunningham's, as I see it. Just goes to show you that skill in merchandising is not at all the same thing as skill in getting cooperation.

Offhand, I'd say that Cunningham would have to stop

using some of his specialized sales skills in conferences and concentrate on finding ways to let others pick up some credit for contributing to his idea. That habit of his, for instance, of scrutinizing a person's face for signs of reaction is too obvious in a conference situation; he should, of course, be extremely observant, but a clumsy showing of tactics like that can make people uneasy and resistant. Also, Cunningham's strong diplomatic tendencies can get him into trouble in handling someone like Poglia, who seems to be nursing resentments of various kinds. I'll be waiting to hear what you find out from Poglia and Fargo. And don't forget that any recommendations that occur to you will be welcome, too. Carry on!

PHIL CADMUS

TO:     Mr. Philip Cadmus

FROM:   Tom Beekman

Your comments on my last received just before I went in to see Poglia this morning and they have helped a great deal, I can tell you, not only in talking with Poglia but in assessing my meeting with Fargo yesterday. Guess I'd been a bit taken in by Cunningham's smooth performance at that rocky conference yesterday. Will henceforth try to be more cautious.

Fargo appears to me to be one of those gruff-mannered, plain-spoken men who repeatedly rub people the wrong way, and most of the time he does it consciously, as a kind of defense against the criticisms of himself that he seems to expect from everyone. This trait seems to have hurt him in his career at Plaston, for he told me, quite frankly, of the high hopes he had had of getting ahead when he joined the company. I was surprised at his openness on this score until I realized that he was expecting me to take the "true story of things at the plant" back to headquarters where, he says, "action can be taken." He spent several years under Cunningham as a route salesman, but would constantly blast off at Cunningham who, he says, is "a goddam show-off" whenever the top brass is around. Cunningham, I gathered, never let these blasts bother him much, on the spot, but Fargo did not get many raises and five years ago, after a harsh argument with Cunningham over his expense account, Fargo went to Peebles and asked to be transferred out of the sales department. Peebles moved him into the traffic department, where Fargo seems to have done very well; he works hard to please the customers, he says, and a couple of years ago Peebles appointed him head of Traffic when that department's aging chief retired. Fargo's friction with the accounting department seems to stem from the trouble he had justifying his expense accounts as a salesman; he clearly has no love for Poglia, the department head—calls him "a tight-fisted dago."

I tried to draw Fargo out on the subject of Cunningham's proposal, but he was apathetic. Said he himself had suggested the idea to Cunningham some months ago when a couple of customers kept asking for different-sized panels, but Cunningham had tossed the suggestion aside. Now I see, of course, where Cunningham failed in his conference yesterday so far as Fargo is concerned. If he'd let Fargo have the credit for suggesting it, and had asked Fargo for his advice on putting the idea over, Cunningham might have had at least one very cooperative colleague. I begin to think that Cunningham is rather a small-bore manager, and I have a new respect for Fargo though I don't think he will go much higher in the company. Fargo has, in my opinion, the quality of dependability that carries out the job in spite of personal antagonisms. Given a little appreciation, I would guess he'd knock himself out to cooperate and deliver the goods.

My talk with Poglia this morning was not so satisfying. He is a calculating type who gives the impression of having things figured out ahead of everyone else. When I asked about his past experience in the company, he replied, "Accounting department for fifteen years, period." It turned out he spent a good stretch on accounting at night school, after high school, and had since taken correspondence courses as well. On a hunch, I asked him what he thought of Cunningham, and he said, "Oh, he's O.K., I guess, only he's like all salesmen, never thinks beforehand about what anything is likely to cost." I pushed further by asking what Poglia liked to do for fun, in the evenings, and he almost beamed at me. Said he liked the theatre, and especially now that his daughter had become good at the ballet; seems she recently was picked to lead the dance chorus in a suburban stock company. Then I saw him frown slightly, and I asked if anything was wrong. He looked at me hard for a moment, but didn't answer, so I changed the subject back to the company, particularly back to the president's program for cost saving.

Poglia warmed up to this in a different way, and quickly gave me a run-down on the planning and control program he was trying to install in the plant. His big trouble, he said, is getting Peebles to cooperate in the program. Poglia thought Peebles was far too lenient with supervisors and foremen who didn't make departmental bogeys. According to Poglia, productivity was way off from the standards set up by time studies. I asked if Peebles' men had handled the time studies and learned, to my surprise, that these were strictly under the jurisdiction of Accounting. Why hadn't Poglia openly asked Peebles to cooperate in the control program? "Why should I?" Poglia said. "Has he ever asked us to help him with anything?"

Obviously a quarrel of long standing, and fairly typical.

I didn't press the matter, and he seemed relieved to have me leave. As he showed me out to the main hall, we passed a middle-aged woman who smiled at Poglia and said, "Congratulations on Nancy's new role!" and then added, "She should do beautifully with Betty." Poglia forced a thin smile, and nodded to the woman; and in an attempt to make some small talk as we parted, I said, "Is Betty another star performer in your family?" Poglia glared at me and snapped, "No." And that ended things between us. Later in the afternoon I learned from Gately that Betty was Cunningham's daughter, and she had been given the solo part in the same ballet that Poglia's daughter was in. So there's another obstacle that Cunningham will have to overcome if he's going to get cooperation from Poglia.

You have asked me for recommendations that occur to me, and all I can say at the moment is that the more I learn about this Plaston situation, the more I wonder whether any solution is really going to eliminate these built-in frictions. Seems to me if you changed these men so they would cooperate, you'd have an entirely different company, in effect, and it might be a company that President Hegeman wouldn't want to be connected with any more. But I forget that in order to change these men, you'd also have to change Hegeman to a large degree. Perhaps after I've talked with Cunningham tomorrow, I'll have an idea worth presenting to you. Regards.

Том

TO: Tom Beekman

I thought I detected a slight note of resignation in your last report, Tom, and I just want to let you know that that may be a good sign that you're finally getting a close grip on this problem. Darkest before dawn, you know, or, as the inventor might have it, frustration before inspiration. Maybe your talk with Cunningham will produce the first ray of real light on the situation, but I think you've already collected enough data to indicate what a solution of Plaston's troubles might be. For instance, you've determined that Poglia's attitudes stem from President Hegeman's "frame of reference," as the psychologists say; and you've also established some of the reasons why both Poglia and Fargo are suffering status pains in their egos. I'm sure your talk with Cunningham will be fruitful, one way or another. Wait and see. Regards.

PHIL CADMUS

TO:     Mr. Philip Cadmus

FROM:  Tom Beekman

Thanks for the boost to my morale. Guess I did get a bit gloomy about the prospects here at Plaston, but, as you predicted, my talk with Cunningham produced things that have bounced me back on the hopeful side.

I'll start with Cunningham's views about himself, because these seem to me the most encouraging aspects of this whole situation. There is no doubt that Cunningham regards himself as a good deal less than first-rate as a conference chairman; he said he thought he had goofed badly in letting Poglia and Fargo scrap as they did, and he also pointed out that he had annoyed Peebles by his clumsy requests for comments. Cunningham admitted these things in a serious, remorseful way, and he seems genuinely intent on improving his conference behavior. I asked him if he thought it advisable to approach everybody diplomatically, as though they were customers, and his reply surprised me: "If you'd asked me that a while ago I'd have said, 'you're damn right I do.'

I've always sold merchandise that way. But I'm beginning
to think this approach may be wrong." What had given him
this idea, I asked. Cunningham told me right off that "that
fellow Poglia woke me up," and he went on to explain that
he'd been trying for months to rub Poglia the right way,
looking for favors he could do for him, etc., but Poglia never
warmed up. Then Cunningham tried to soothe Poglia after
that last conference by asking him questions. Cunningham
had read somewhere that "questions are powerful antidotes
for hostility." The questions Cunningham asked weren't
hard, he said, and he found he could ask them without any
effort at being "diplomatic." In fact, the more he asked, the
more it seemed that Poglia was ready to answer. Cunningham said the first thing he knew he was actually getting interested in what Poglia was saying, and when he finally left
Poglia, the latter had voluntarily offered to supply him with
some analytical projections on the market for these new
plastic panels. "You could have knocked me over," Cunningham said.

Anyway, Cunningham is so impressed by this "discovery"
of his about asking questions that he's going to practice it
further. I asked Cunningham how interested he was in people as people, not as customers; in the ways they reacted, the
things they liked and disliked, etc. He said he guessed he
was "as interested as the next fellow," which meant that he
"didn't usually take the time to find out about people." I
asked him if his salesmen often asked him for help on their
prospects, and Cunningham said almost never. Then he apparently saw the connection himself, shook his head, and
said, "Damned if I ever thought of it like that."

We talked a little about his personal life, which seems
quite ordinary—suburban friends, golf, socially busy wife,
etc.—he proudly talked about his daughter Betty and her

ballet lessons. I found out Cunningham didn't even know Poglia had a daughter, much less that she was to be in the same ballet program with his daughter. But I didn't let him know about Poglia's hurt pride in this connection. Didn't think it was any of my business.

Well, that gives you the substance of my interview with Cunningham. I think his attitude is most commendable and, I repeat, encouraging so far as his getting cooperation at Plaston is concerned. Now I am anxious to see him in action at the second meeting of this group set for tomorrow morning. I've got an idea for your consideration, but will hold until after I've checked it out at this meeting. Regards.

TOM BEEKMAN

TO: Tom Beekman

Your report on Cunningham makes me feel a bit repentant about my earlier remarks on his weaknesses. Frankly, I'm delighted you found him so ready to take a look at himself and learn things. Allow me to congratulate you on your own questioning, incidentally. Nice going. And I think you were right not to speak to Cunningham about Poglia's hurt pride on the ballet matter; that's a wound for him to discover and try to heal, if he wants to. If you tipped him off, he probably wouldn't learn as much from the situation.

Conference #2 should be a darb. I'll be waiting impatiently.

PHIL CADMUS

TO:    Mr. Philip Cadmus

FROM: Tom Beekman

After all the build-up I've given you about the second conference, which Cunningham held today, perhaps I should apologize for the lack of dramatics. Briefly, here's the way things went: Cunningham opened briskly, as before, with greetings all around, and then reminded them that the last meeting had turned out "null and void," for which he was largely to blame. I thought this was a kind of negative start, but Cunningham immediately sparked their attention by reporting he had "had a talk with the president," who wanted Cunningham to give the others a "message." The message was that President Hegeman was counting on each one of these men to "come up with the very best ideas each had" to meet the present competition, which all of them know is getting very stiff.

This message could have fallen just as flat as any other pep talk from the boss if Cunningham hadn't at once pitched in with his questions. His first one was: "Does anyone here object if I just withdraw right now and scratch the idea I spoke about last week?" There were some smiles, and Fargo goaded him with "Better late than never!" But Cunningham remained earnest, and said nothing. There was a noticeable pause and then Peebles said he thought maybe they "could salvage something" out of Cunningham's idea. This slight indication of generosity seemed slowly to affect the mood of the others, for Fargo and Poglia in turn began to comment on ways that Cunningham's idea might be salvaged. (Gately said nothing; apparently Cunningham had dressed him down proper after his blunders of the last meeting.)

As each man contributed a suggestion, Cunningham sat listening, nodding now and then, and asking questions for as much information as he thought each man could deliver. After quite a while of this, Cunningham announced he was "amazed at the way you boys manhandled my brain child," which he said he "couldn't begin to recognize any more." Then he suggested that each of the others "take your own ideas and see if you want to add or change anything before we send them to Hegeman next week." The others saw they were going to be identified with their own suggestions, and they obviously liked it. Cunningham ended the meeting at this point, and the other men (except Gately, who stuck beside Cunningham) walked out talking busily with each other.

Well, I think Cunningham at least started some cooperation, and in my opinion he's learned fast. In view of what he accomplished, I am embarrassed to report on that idea I was going to submit for your consideration, but I might as well make a clean breast of it. I was going to suggest that we persuade these five men to try that technique which Harvard's Roethlisberger recommends for improving communication—i.e., make each man repeat the idea of any other person whom he intends to answer or criticize, and repeat it so that his statement satisfies the other person. This gimmick ought to work, but I somehow feel that with inflammable men like Fargo, and needlers like Poglia, one could run into a lot of trouble with it. Agree?

My latest proposal therefore is simply that Cunningham be encouraged to keep on doing what he's doing. Right or wrong? Regards.

TOM BEEKMAN

TO: Tom Beekman
    Hotel Brunswick
    Lancaster, Pa.

RE: Cooperation at Plaston

Answering your final query: Right you are. There's a lot more to be done to ensure harmony among Plaston's people in Lancaster, but you may leave with a clear conscience: your present assignment has been completed with distinction. See you Monday at the office.

PHIL CADMUS

P.S. Can you bring home some shoo-fly pie?

# CHAPTER FOUR

# Initiative-Ambition-Drive

*There has been considerable moaning among some students of management—and among some top executives—that young men today are seriously lacking in initiative, particularly the kind that shows up in a willingness to assume more responsibility. In the old days, so the stories go, a young man worth his salt had the get up and go to reach the top, to make a lot of money, to become famous; but nowadays, the cliché runs, "all they want is security." The indictment is no truer than any other sociological generalization. The fact is that successful executives now show initiative, ambition, and drive, but they show these—and expect these to be shown—in many, many different ways. A popular description of a man with initiative today is one who is "a self-starter." But an executive may identify this trait with planning and the patient achievement of objectives; or with courage to act; or with "creativeness"; or with an inquiring mind; or with making suggestions; or with dissatisfaction with the status quo; or with interest in*

*profits and new ideas; or with unselfish helpfulness.
And the meanings of ambition and drive have become similarly diverse.*

*In this chapter, the varieties of these three
closely related traits are set forth in an imaginary
diary kept by an experienced management consultant. His notes are much more embellished and far
less telegraphic than those a consultant in real life
might jot down; but his observations and opinions
are authentic.*

**Thursday, July 12**

Just returned from a session with Outerbridge of Placoid
Corp., who is taking time out as president to look for a replacement for Maddox, his manufacturing vice president.
That's primarily Maddox's job, but it's the kind of thing Outerbridge gets all wound up in. Outerbridge says he called me
in to get "an outsider's viewpoint." The trouble in this case
seems to be chiefly Outerbridge's prejudices, a problem I've
grown all too familiar with in my twelve years of trouble
shooting for this company. He's sixty-seven himself but calls
Maddox, who's sixty-two, a "gruff old dictator," and is annoyed that Maddox has already picked his own assistant,
Delucci, to take over as manufacturing v.p. As I recall,
Delucci is a diplomatic, polished, and able man—now would
be in his early forties—who has been Maddox's man Friday
for ten years. But Outerbridge says Delucci doesn't have any
initiative. "For that job," Outerbridge insists, "I want a man
who's a self-starter." Sometimes Outerbridge says Delucci
hasn't got enough ambition; and sometimes he says Delucci
doesn't have enough drive. But Maddox seems to think Delucci has plenty of initiative, ambition, and drive. Looks like

my main job this time will be to find out what Outerbridge
and Maddox think these words mean. Maybe they're both
wrong about Delucci.

When I asked Outerbridge what he meant by these words,
he was pretty fast with his answers. He said, "A man with
initiative has creativeness, which boils down to a willingness
to accept responsibility and risks"; by drive he means "dissatisfaction with the status quo"; and by ambition he means
"self-confidence and an eagerness to train for more responsibility." Didn't question any of these definitions, but suspect
they are a mixture of what he has read in some book and the
owner-manager ideas he's inherited from his father. But he
isn't too much like his father.

The company psychologist, I recall, once described Outerbridge the founder as "a remote, primordial father," and
the full portrait, as nearly as I can remember the psychologist's words, was "a Biblical figure with Ivy-college education and tastes who wanted to spread the company's message
of service." Both the company and the industry have out-
grown that sort of person, but the son still behaves like his
father occasionally. The psychologist said Outerbridge had
not shown his father's "basic compulsion to impose his ideas
on the external world—that is, on others." But according to
the psychologist, the son has always felt compelled to make
good in the family firm, and so insists on making many decisions for his subordinates; doesn't trust their judgment.
These personal traits are bad for the company, the psychologist thinks.

Personally, I'm not so sure he's right. Initiative has always been essential at the top, and the boss, one way or
another, has to keep shaping his subordinates' judgment.
Nowadays, industrial psychologists take a dim view of
authoritarian figures, but I always notice that any well-run
business seems to have a lot of them around.

**Monday, July 16**

Walking through the shop today I ran into Joe, the time-study man, and seeing him reminded me not to take Outer-bridge too literally when he says he wants his subordinates to show "creativeness" by being willing to accept risks and responsibility. Outerbridge conveniently forgets how tough he's been on those who have been *too* "creative"—i.e., those who have assumed responsibility without keeping informed and exercising discretion. For instance, the time he canned one of Joe's favorites, a first-class production engineer, and also a bright individualist, who took the responsibility of putting a few hard facts into a luncheon speech he gave before the local chapter of the S.A.M. This engineer had described in enthusiastic terms the company's success with a new work-measurement technique, and then went on to say that before this new technique was adopted, the company was slowly going broke with rising labor costs. This happened to be true. But the poor chap wasn't savvy: he somehow didn't know that Outerbridge had for months been planning to finance an expansion program with a new issue of preferred, and had been assuring his bankers that the company was in A1 shape. When the paper reported the engineer's statement, of course, Outerbridge was furious and publicly denied the story; then he had the fellow fired for "violating company regulations."

That phrase he used about drive being "dissatisfaction with the status quo" could be equally misleading. It all depends on how much dissatisfaction a fellow chooses to show, and when. Outerbridge would sure be annoyed if any young manager spoke up too boldly at one of his monthly luncheon conferences. Suppose he criticized the way the company keeps making that old line of products which kept it out of the red back in the Thirties and which "made" the sales v.p. As a result, the sales v.p. is still sentimental about the

line, even though it's become a built-in money-loser. Outerbridge knows it's losing money too, of course, but he long
ago told me it's a small price to pay for sustaining his temper-
amental sales vice president's morale. If the company
dropped the line altogether, this man might begin to feel
shelved, and Outerbridge says he can still get a lot of mileage
out of the guy.

What Outerbridge means by both initiative and drive obviously includes large helpings of judgment. To a large extent, that means keeping in line with Outerbridge's biases,
values, and tastes. Never will forget the time Maddox told
the boss and the sales vice president that he thought the
new streamlined model the design department had submitted
looked like "an idiot's brain child." For a second Outerbridge
looked pleased all over, apparently because he thought so
too. But he was smart, and recovered fast. He knew the
sales v.p., though he can be sentimental about some obsolete
product, can also get very excited about a brand-new one.
So Outerbridge began to kid Maddox for his provincial
tastes, thus soothing the sales v.p., who had been heating
up and bristling to defend the new model. Later, Outerbridge made so many strong "suggestions" about the model
that it was finally scrapped. Some designer's initiative was
also probably badly blunted.

It's this kind of thing that makes me realize why Outerbridge really doesn't want the manufacturing vice presidency
taken over by Maddox's assistant, Delucci. He admires
Maddox enormously and wants another tough, outspoken
character like him in this slot, not a man he thinks may try
to win his favor with diplomacy and a smoothly administered
department. I'd say he wants an aggressive manager who
is not afraid to say no, who has the push to get the work
out no matter what, and who is ambitious enough to make
personal sacrifices that may improve his behavior as a mana-

ger. On this last point, at least, Maddox's assistant doesn't
seem to measure up; I remember that Delucci declined Outerbridge's suggestion that he go to Harvard Business School
for a stretch. Delucci doesn't look much like the driving,
aggressive type. But I keep wondering why Maddox, who is
certainly shrewd, is so insistent on having Delucci succeed
him. Better find out tomorrow.

**Tuesday, July 17**

The discussion I had with the manufacturing v.p. today
was a real eye opener. Maddox is an extremely wary, hard-
ened bird, who I understand from several directors is down
to become president before he retires. Right off the bat he
said he guessed I was wondering why he picked Delucci to
succeed him. A nice opening move on his part, too: for one
thing, it was true, and it showed he knew I tended to agree
with what the president thought of Delucci, and that Maddox
was ready to argue with both of us. I admitted I was puzzled
by his choice, said I respected his judgment, etc. He smiled
at me and then made a sharp crack: said he knew that I knew
where my bread was buttered. A cocky fellow, all right;
doesn't seem the least bit worried as to how I might report on
him. Knows Outerbridge wouldn't dare get rid of him after
all these years.

Of course, his remark burned me a bit, but I am old
enough at this game to be able to shake off such slaps and
get on with my work. I asked him whether he thought his
assistant had enough real initiative and drive to take over
the top manufacturing job. His reply was pretty insulting.
"Sure he does, but could be it's not the kind a consultant
knows about." This crack I also ignored, and just let him go
on to tell me what he thought "real initiative" was.

This turned out to be several different things. One was
Delucci's ability to "act fast in all the facets of his job."

Another was Delucci's interest in profits and new ideas. Maddox said his protégé could track down a shop variance faster than anyone he had ever known, and was just as fast at setting up new procedures to get a new model into the line. Also he said Delucci is "a real self-starter who never needs any prodding and is loaded with drive." When I asked what he meant by drive, he said this was simply the ability to keep pushing on the job for long stretches. "Delucci has a healthy appetite for work," he added. "You might even say he's an eager beaver."

But how far would Maddox let Delucci go in solving problems on his own? His reply to this would probably have burned Outerbridge, who rarely likes to hear others express the kind of opinion his father used to deliver. "Oh, Delucci isn't kidding himself about what the boss calls 'creative' ideas. That's a lot of crap. Delucci knows the ropes, the way I like things done. He's really dedicated to his job." Then he went on to cite the time when the boss suggested Delucci go to Harvard Business School. "Delucci and I talked it over," he said, "and we agreed completely that Delucci would learn a lot more management right here in the shop than he would up at Harvard listening to professors' theories and chewing the fat with other managers." I asked Maddox how he managed to convince Outerbridge of this. He laughed and said he really didn't try to; he just told Outerbridge that he and Delucci agreed that the idea was worth thinking about, but that the shop couldn't possibly spare Delucci right at that time. And Outerbridge went along with him. Only mentioned the idea once again about a year later, when Maddox found it even easier to convince him that Delucci couldn't be spared.

The more Maddox talked about Delucci, the more he seemed to be protecting him, treating him like a son. I asked him what he thought Delucci's ambitions were, and he said without a moment's hesitation, "To take over my job." How did he know this? Delucci had told him so several times. In so many words? It turned out that, to Maddox, Delucci had clearly shown his ambition whenever he had remarked on what an important job the manufacturing vice president had. I nearly laughed out loud at this one. Maddox sure finds it hard to imagine that Delucci might aspire to any other job in the company.

Decided to try to find out what Maddox's own "level of aspiration" is, and asked him what the word ambition meant to him, hoping he might reveal one of his own. He said, "Ambition is the desire to get ahead, to earn more money and more recognition in one's field." Sounds to me as though it came right out of some management manual. Did he think a manager ought to make sacrifices for the sake of the company? He said he guessed so, but insisted that "the solid rewards of money and title have to be there, too." Would he want to be president? Of course he would, but he said he wasn't making any special effort to "develop" himself for the job. He figures his boss and the directors will do the picking when the time comes, and is relying on his company record to win him the presidency. What would his ambitions be if he became president? This appeared to puzzle Maddox momentarily and he passed it off with a very pat phrase about "helping the company grow and make money."

I know psychoanalysts who would smile at this answer and claim that Maddox was covering up his "aggressive drive for power over others." But it doesn't seem to be quite that simple. I think that when Maddox says he wants to help the company grow he may honestly be stating at least part of his ambition. That book by Lauterbach on motives and money makes a lot of good points, and I agree that instead of wealth and power, status and security certainly seem to be the prime goals of an awful lot of executives these days. But in my opinion such men haven't yet reached the topmost level of executive functioning—and not too many do. They are still anxious about themselves and haven't yet developed the kind of self-confidence that comes when ambition evolves into a desire for things that do not directly or materially reward the personal self. Professor Paul Pigors of M.I.T. once put it rather neatly: "Great executives don't have personal ambition." Agree emphatically.

### Wednesday, July 18

Talked this afternoon to the manufacturing v.p.'s assistant, Delucci. As I suspected, neither Outerbridge nor Maddox described him very well. Both looked at him through their own self-colored glasses, so to speak. A nice fellow on the whole, I think. Has what I consider real drive. He said he'd started bucking for the assistant's job when he realized he was getting lost in the engineering department, where there were too many competing technicians and too few good management jobs. Delucci started sending suggestions about products and models to the manufacturing division, and one day he got a call to "go see the manufacturing v.p."

During the talk about one of Delucci's suggestions (he can't remember what it was), Maddox tore the idea to shreds. Delucci said he felt his anger rising but he kept quiet, and didn't say much after the v.p. went on to describe some of his own ideas. But when he described one idea that seemed first-rate to Delucci, Delucci said so, emphatically. That apparently softened Maddox up. As the talk continued, Delucci criticized the sales department for its failure to recognize good ideas, and Maddox warmed up to the point where he asked if Delucci would consider going to work for him. Here Delucci showed his tactical skill; said he wouldn't take this job, attractive though it was, unless it would bring him some real dough. That really fetched Maddox, who is from Texas and very money-minded.

Delucci says that as Maddox's assistant he has confined himself almost exclusively to taking care of administrative details such as personnel assignments, overtime, grievances, variances, etc. He was careful not to assume any responsibilities that Maddox liked to handle, such as production rates and quality control. When the v.p. was out of town, Delucci would be sure to backstop him, particularly on production data that the president had already asked for and wanted in a hurry. This meant Delucci spent a lot of time becoming skilled in practically everything that went into and out of Maddox's office.

I asked Delucci if Maddox gave him credit for his assists, and was surprised to learn that Delucci had adroitly covered up these actions or else credited them to others. Delucci said he felt sure that although his boss would have given him credit for these things, he would have given it grudgingly, and might even have begun to suspect Delucci of trying to show him up. Delucci says he purposely agreed with Maddox that he ought not to go to Harvard Business School, as Outerbridge had suggested. He would have enjoyed the course but wasn't ready to risk antagonizing his "patron." This is "controlled aggressiveness," all right.

Delucci has an interesting slant on the president. Thinks Outerbridge wouldn't recognize "real initiative" if he saw it, because he has never really had to show any himself. Under the founder, the company had long ago monopolized its biggest market with its patented insulator, which still provides two-thirds of its profits. And the founder's son has been content to ride along in the same groove. If he'd had initiative, Delucci says, he would have done something to stop the company's profit margins from slipping all these

years while sales have kept rising. A merger right now with
Y. & B. Co., Delucci thinks, would shoot some real juice into
management's tired blood and wake the president up to new
marketing and production techniques. But Delucci's afraid
Outerbridge may be too old and tired for this kind of thing.

Who could snap the company out of it, then? That's easy,
Delucci says; he thinks *he* could. Well, he's got ambition all
right. Delucci thought I was surprised at his boast, and
quickly added that he was quite aware he was caught under
the manufacturing v.p. for the present; and he suspected
the president doesn't think he's so hot. In his opinion the
president seems likely to pick, as the next manufacturing
v.p., that jet-propelled bustler, John L. Royt, who has recently been running the scheduling department.

Delucci lost no time filling me in on Royt. He's an openly
ambitious, restless, and impatient driver, according to Delucci. Royt is thirty-eight, the son of a small hardware dealer.
Delucci says Royt makes very impetuous decisions. Also says
the man never misses a chance to make an impression on
Outerbridge. For instance, Royt got wind of an inquiry last
month about a hot new gismo for which the model hadn't
even been released to engineering by the design department.
But Royt thought he saw a chance to show initiative; did
some snooping in the design department, then passed word
about the new gismo along to Vibrissa Corp., a pampered old
customer he's been handling.

This backfired pretty quickly when Maddox heard that
Vibrissa was trying to order the gismo. He chewed Royt
out but good for leaking the news, since it turned out that
Sudoral Co. had been given an exclusive option on the gismo.
Sudoral was so mad at the leak it canceled its whole original
secret order. Then Vibrissa also canceled. This whole incident is about as classic a case of "indiscriminate initiative"
as I've ever seen.

Unfortunately, according to Delucci, Royt seems to have kept the original credit for "creativeness" he got when Outerbridge first heard Royt's initiative praised by an old crony, Vibrissa's president. Royt probably has the kind of push Outerbridge admires in what he calls "enterprising Americans."

**Thursday, July 19**

Since yesterday I've been puzzling over Delucci's ideas about initiative. He seemed content to play his part quietly under Maddox and, for my money, seemed much too calm about the fact that Royt is favored to cop the v.p.'s job. So I went back and talked to Delucci again this afternoon, and now I'm inclined to give him an A plus for "controlled aggressiveness." Delucci disclosed his strategy to me only after he seemed convinced that I was friendly and not sold on Royt. He knew I might change sides, but he was willing to take this risk, which in itself is a nice symptom of initiative.

Briefly, Delucci said he intended to stick close to his patron, Maddox, who is practically certain to succeed Outerbridge as president. Then Delucci hoped to become the president's assistant and as nearly indispensable as he could make himself. Delucci not only figures Maddox will depend on him to handle all personnel matters, just as he'd handled union negotiation and personnel grievances in the shop; Delucci also expects to guide Maddox through the sales and marketing jungles, which are now almost unknown territory to him. By the time his patron's retirement date rolled around, Delucci thought his own qualifications would be clearly recognized by the directors.

But meanwhile what about Royt? Delucci isn't worried. He says he calculates that Royt will wind up the way a friend of his at the Mitral Plastic Co. did. This fellow, Delucci says, "always has both elbows out" and his aggression overshadowed all possible rivals. He spent money wildly and continually irritated associates, but the top brass forgave this because they liked his aggressive salesmanship and kept promoting him right on up to be assistant to the general manager. But when this bull in a china shop started to make big decisions for the general manager, the general manager finally said he couldn't take it any more. The company still didn't want to lose him, so the fellow was sent out to Chicago, as a special divisional vice president, but it was really a dead-end staff job.

Delucci's gamble looks good. These fellows like Royt usually thrash around, take charge, make decisions—right or wrong—until they are moved up or out. They look hot for a while, but I've seen many of them burnt out in their fifties. I'm generally inclined to bet on quiet, foresighted planners like Delucci, who don't continually need their egos pampered. Delucci is no fireball, and both his initiative and ambition are now rather narrowly centered on his promotion strategy. But he's got the kind of lasting drive and personal flexibility that Royt, I think, obviously lacks.

**Friday, July 20**
Managed to catch Royt for a half-hour today, probably because a long lunch with the boss had slowed him down a bit. He certainly pushes himself hard. Even when he's thinking out an answer he seems to be on the run, anxious to get on to other things. But he was immediately on his guard when I brought up the subject of the manufacturing job. Guess Outerbridge has been talking to him confidentially already.

Testing a bit, I asked Royt what he'd do if he didn't land this vice presidency, and he shot back that he wasn't bothering to think about such things. Said he wanted the job very much and was sure he had what it took. How so? He ran through a few of his experiences in a big department store where he spent a couple of years before he joined Placoid.

You are expected to push your way around in the retailing game, of course, and Royt liked it. "Maybe it was tough at times on some men," he recalled, "but in any business your own skin is what counts." He said that the head of the department store used to talk to him about being too aggressive and ambitious, but Royt knew they liked a man to be "a real self-starter" and would try to hold him down only until they found the right spot for him.

Then why didn't he stay in retailing? He said frankly that he didn't enjoy the type of men he had to work with there, and by "right type" Royt says he means college-educated, good family background, and "socially acceptable." Royt is confident he'll get the manufacturing vice presidency, but admitted he was really aiming for the presidency. He grinned patronizingly when I mentioned Delucci as a potential competitor for the job. He thinks Delucci's "an awful nice guy," but too easygoing.

Royt says showing initiative is not so much taking the lead in things as having the nerve to take on more and more responsibility. When he was offered a chance by Outerbridge to become a Sloan fellow at M.I.T., he grabbed it; he knew it would be tough going, but it would practically ensure his getting a top job in the company in a very short time. Royt said he knew you had to be ready to take the rap for your own mistakes. "You just keep driving," he says, "no matter what happens." I noticed he had smoked parts of three cigarettes just in the time we had been talking. Begin to wonder how long he can hold his present pace.

**Tuesday, July 24**

Presented my recommendation to Outerbridge this A.M. that Delucci be selected to succeed Maddox as manufacturing v.p. Outerbridge not at all pleased, and began arguing for "someone with drive and ambition." I asked him if he had anyone particular in mind, and he immediately named

Royt. I then gave him my reasons for suspecting that Royt wouldn't do in this job, but I don't think Outerbridge really heard me. At any rate, he just said there still was time to give the matter some more thought.

**Thursday, August 16**

Early this afternoon I got a call from Grundhofer, one of the directors, asking me to attend a special board meeting at Placoid Corp. today at 3:00 P.M. When I arrived I learned from Grundhofer that the board last week had decided to move Outerbridge up to the chairmanship, and put Maddox in as president, as soon as a new manufacturing v.p. could be installed. The board felt, and Outerbridge agreed, that before Maddox retired he deserved at least three years as chief executive officer. But this decision had brought a real showdown between Outerbridge and Maddox over Maddox's replacement, and the board wanted my recommendations. Both Outerbridge and Maddox were at the meeting.

When I told the board that Delucci appeared to be the most competent man available to succeed Maddox, giving the same reasons I'd given to Outerbridge, Outerbridge looked extremely annoyed, and as soon as I finished he spoke up. He said flatly that as board chairman and majority stockholder he could not bring himself to trust the company's manufacturing division to Delucci. Maddox grumbled, but before he could say anything, one of the directors broke the tension by suggesting that a committee be appointed to "explore the situation further," and report back to the board. A three-man committee was immediately named and the meeting adjourned.

**Monday, August 27**

Today I was updated on the Maddox replacement problem. The board's three-man committee called at my office and told me that in view of the deadlock between Out-

erbridge and Maddox they had decided to get an outsider
to fill the manufacturing vice presidency. One man on the
committee said he had proposed that I be offered the job!
The two others said that good consultants almost never make
good operating executives. I said they were quite right about
the limitations of consultants, and congratulated the committee on its good judgment. They then asked me about a
man named Waldman who was running Garget Corp.'s
manufacturing division. I knew Waldman and described him
as a brilliant production operator but one who had a reputation for job-hopping.

**Wednesday, September 12**

A phone call today from Outerbridge informed me that
the board had just voted to hire Waldman to succeed
Maddox. Seems that Waldman will be able to leave Garget
Corp. in less than a month. Well, I hope he stays at Placoid
long enough to show Outerbridge how hard it's going to be
for any man to operate under Maddox if Maddox doesn't
like him.

**Friday, November 2**

Paid a brief call on Outerbridge this afternoon, to see how
things were coming along regarding Waldman. Appears that
Waldman has already joined Placoid and has taken hold
fast. But he turned out to be straight poison to Royt. Waldman has a cold, domineering way about him. Apparently
Royt blew up three times just in the first week Waldman was
on the job. Outerbridge had spoken to Waldman and had
tried to smooth Royt down, but three days ago Royt got so
mad at Waldman that he really blew his stack, called Waldman a number of vulgar names, and walked right off the job.

I asked how Delucci was taking Waldman, and gathered
that Delucci doesn't like Waldman much either, but Outer-

bridge wouldn't elaborate. Went down to the shop floor and
learned from Joe, the time-study man, that Delucci is managing to keep his temper under control; Delucci had made a
point of going right in to Waldman the day he arrived, and
offered his cooperation in whatever changes Waldman
wanted. Apparently Delucci was the only manager under
Waldman who did this, and Waldman now consults him
fairly regularly. Waldman has just sent him on a trip to the
West Coast.

**Friday, November 16**

Finally had good chat with Delucci this morning. He said
he doesn't find Waldman so hard to get along with, but
doesn't admire the way Waldman cuts corners to save
money. At the same time, Delucci told me he's now helping Maddox over weekends, assisting him with his presidential paperwork. Maddox obviously is still determined to
get Delucci as an assistant. But as Delucci and Maddox now
both know, Maddox will have to win over the three directors
who joined Outerbridge at a recent board meeting when they
vetoed the establishment of a presidential assistant's job.
Delucci is confident he'll get this job fairly soon; he has
already drawn up a job description on it for the company
manual.

**Monday, November 19**

When I told Outerbridge this afternoon about Delucci
and his extracurricular activities, he grunted and said, "Delucci is sure ambitious, bucking for an assistant's job that
doesn't even exist." Funny thing, but Outerbridge still thinks
Delucci lacks drive and initiative.

CHAPTER FIVE   *Decisiveness*

*The quality of decisiveness, or the ability to make
decisions, has been repeatedly nominated as the
trait that most clearly distinguishes the real executive. This does not seem to be the fact; but it is
sure that a manager who lacked this capacity would
scarcely function as an executive. The capacity,
however, is not to be confused with the old-fashioned autocratic order giving that was presumed to
be characteristic of all executives in an earlier era.
Nor is the difficult act of business decision to be
identified with those mechanical, mathematical
decisions supplied through such techniques as
operations research, linear programing, electronic
data processing, etc. These techniques are, of
course, a great assistance in broadening the limited
judgments of men; but they are incapable of the
endless variety of subtle decisions that every competent executive is expected to reach, and are
particularly useless in reaching those decisions that
are most difficult and important of all—the decisions that grievously test the character and understanding of the decider.*

*In this chapter some of the difficulties and nuances of executive decision making are presented through the fictionalized correspondence between the president and a new assistant to the president of an electric manufacturing company.*

TO: Mr. Waite

RE: EDP Installation

The controller's office has completed those rough estimates you asked for on the proposed electronic data-processing installation. Mr. Higgins tells me that the figures he gave me over the phone are provisional; while he thinks they're somewhat high, he doesn't consider them too much out of line with the costs he's heard quoted by other controllers on similar installations.

Here are the estimates on the major items:

| | |
|---|---|
| Programing | $250,000 |
| Coding data | $195,000 |
| Site preparation | $100,000 |
| Computer | $1,500,000 |
| Monthly operating costs | $60,000 |

Mr. Higgins points out that renting a big computer will run to approximately the same figure as the amortization charges on an outright purchase. He also asked me to inform you that the installation might eventually save the company $50,000 a month in reduced personnel costs.

FRED GROSVENOR

FROM THE PRESIDENT'S DESK:

TO:    Mr. Grosvenor

Tell Higgins we'll need a lot more information on that EDP job he's proposing to install in the accounting department. What kind of data is it going to process? Who will use this information? What personnel jobs will be cut out if the computer goes in? How long will the installation take? And what's he including under "programing" and "site preparation"? Suggest he check his figures on operating costs; they sound low, judging from what I heard from a friend at the club the other day.

G. B. WAITE

TO: Mr. Waite

RE: EDP Project

I took up your questions on the EDP installation with Mr. Higgins, and he spent some time giving me his answers this morning. He says the computer people have explained to him a number of applications for this equipment, including processing accounts receivable, and providing summaries of sales twice a week. However, he says the immediate application would be in processing payroll data, since tabulations of such data are already available for feeding into the computer. He was not able to give me a specific list of jobs that might be eliminated if the computer were installed, but thinks this eventually might total more than 100 clerical personnel in the sales, purchasing, and accounting departments.

It will take perhaps eighteen months to complete the programing job, the coding job, and the preparation of the "site," i.e., building proper quarters for the computer and related equipment. Higgins says his original estimates on operating costs came from an EDP consultant he talked with, but now he believes those costs might run as high as $75,000 a month.

FRED GROSVENOR

FROM THE PRESIDENT'S DESK:

TO:   Mr. Grosvenor

I have decided not to present the EDP installation project to the executive committee tomorrow morning. Higgins' figures are much too rough, for one thing. We would have to get a feasibility study made, if we were going to consider this thing seriously, but for the present at any rate I believe the company isn't ready for EDP. There is an awful lot of streamlining we can do in our paper work that will save us money right away. I am going to organize a housecleaning project next week to cut down on old forms, clean out old files, etc., etc. Maybe when that's done we can take another look at this EDP business.

One thing we've got to get at right away is this duplication of reports. I found out that thirty-two copies of a single market-research report are being distributed, and there aren't more than five men who ought to be getting it. Also, the accounting department seems to be doing much more checking up on little clerical errors than is justified, according to what I read in Higgins' last monthly report.

I will phone Higgins and explain to him about the decision on the EDP matter, and at the same time ask him to start a survey of the company's paper work and filing routines, forms, etc. We should have this project under way in all departments by the first of the month.

G. B. WAITE

TO: Mr. Waite

RE: EDP Proposal

This morning Mr. Higgins asked me to inform you that a consulting firm has offered to make a feasibility study of the EDP installation at the same time that the company is undertaking its survey of paper work. Mr. Higgins suggests that combining these operations might be productive and time-saving.

FRED GROSVENOR

FROM THE PRESIDENT'S DESK:

TO:    Mr. Grosvenor

You can inform the controller that my decision to postpone the EDP matter for the time being stands as is. I will let him know if and when a feasibility study seems in order.

I trust this decision on the EDP matter does not sound arbitrary to you, but in case it does I feel it would be helpful for you, as my assistant, to understand why it was made. I have already given you some of the more or less technical reasons—e.g., the fact that the company's paper work seems to be in need of drastic overhauling. But there are other reasons why Higgins' proposal is questionable, or at best very premature. Several of these reasons concern the controller himself: he has for a long time been hoping to become a vice president, and some time ago I indirectly heard he was counting on this EDP thing to impress me and the board with the importance of his job. I didn't like the sound of this, but it could have been merely a rumor, so when Higgins finally sent up his proposal I decided to investigate EDP on my own so I could check on Higgins' figures and raise some intelligent questions about the proposal.

As it turned out, my conclusions were much less optimistic than his, and I decided we would be well ahead if we got our paper-work problems straightened out before we undertook a feasibility study. But when Higgins then came back with the suggestion that we accept a consultant's offer to tackle the paper-work job and the feasibility study at the same time, I realized how very intent he must be on getting this EDP job installed. I could have gone along with this suggestion, of course, but decided Higgins had only advanced it in a tactical effort to get me to reconsider his project. If he'd been smarter he might have made this suggestion part of his original proposal, but he apparently didn't want to raise the issue of cleaning up our paper work. Or maybe he didn't know this work ought to be done first. In any case, Higgins didn't prove to me that he'd learned enough about EDP to back up his recommendations solidly, and he also, I think, can use a lesson or two in foresight and patience.

I am sure you will see that in addition there could be other ramifications to this EDP project, such as union objections, that would have to be considered. All in all, my decision to postpone the matter is based on fairly obvious facts and seems entirely logical to me. If all decisions in this company were as easy as this one, I wouldn't feel I was earning my pay.

G. B. WAITE

TO: Mr. Waite

RE: Meeting with Mr. Gibbons of Slick Appliances Inc.

This afternoon Mr. Gibbons brought in a full set of proposals on the merger that his company is asking you to consider. When you spoke with him last week, you recall, he promised to develop five-year estimates on market potential

for their main product, the electric washer and dryer; and
he also was going to consult his treasurer about establishing
a fair market value for the company's stock, which is almost
totally owned by the Gibbons family. Both the market estimates and the market value of the stock are listed on the
attached sheet, which Mr. Gibbons left with me, along with
the formal merger proposals.

In addition, Mr. Gibbons told me that the competitive
situation that Slick Appliances has been struggling with has
become much worse since he talked with you. Two of the
company's major customers, both chain stores for which
Slick has cut prices severely, have suddenly advised him that
they are planning to shift to other manufacturers in order
to ensure the volume of delivery they have been trying to
get from Slick. The loss of the business of these customers
would mean a shutdown for Slick within three months unless
some big new customers could be secured, so Mr. Gibbons is
hopeful that the decision on the proposed merger with us
can be reached as soon as possible. He suggests that any
questions you might have about the merger proposals could
be ironed out quickly at a luncheon conference, with our
lawyers and theirs on hand to draft any changes, etc. Mr.
Gibbons said he would phone you tomorrow to see if this
might be arranged.

                                              FRED GROSVENOR


FROM THE PRESIDENT'S DESK:

TO:   Mr. Grosvenor

Re that merger matter, advise Mr. Gibbons that his
proposals will first have to be studied by our executive committee before we can meet with him and his lawyers.

Since this matter promises to stir up some opposition at
the meeting, you should be fully aware of the situation.

Gibbons and I discussed his proposal by phone the other day. His family has owned Slick Appliances for fifty-five years, but now wants to get out of the business, and expects a decent capital gain out of the merger with us. The company is too small (net worth, about $5 million) to raise the kind of capital it needs to expand its plant the way it should if it is going to meet future competition from the big appliance makers. Slick also badly needs some fresh management talent, especially in marketing; unfortunately none of the younger men in the family have developed too well, while the reputation for nepotism in the company has naturally made it hard for Slick to attract ambitious young managers.

However, Slick has always made a high-quality appliance, and I think a vertical merger with this company would give us a very respectable entry into the consumer field. As you know, I have for some time been convinced that we will have to broaden our operations in the electrical industry in order to keep growing as we should, and I expect to convince the executive committee of this on Friday. This is, however, a serious policy decision that will have to be strongly defended against those on the committee who are sure to bring up counterarguments. Some of these arguments I can anticipate without much trouble. For instance, John Dalt will probably insist that the costs of trying to consolidate the sales staffs, offices, and routines of the two companies will boost our overhead so high we won't be able to maintain profit margins on either Slick's appliances or our own line of motors. Also, Tim Burroughs is likely to oppose this merger because he thinks we should be diversifying through mergers with companies in non-electrical industries. And of course practically all our executives will be naturally anxious about their own future positions in case the merger with Slick goes through.

I am confident I can answer most of the objections the

committee may bring up, but there is still some uncertainty
in my mind about the timing of any merger we might work
out that gets us into the appliance field. On the one hand, we
obviously wouldn't want to lose those two big chain-store
customers who are threatening to shift their business away
from Slick; but we also don't want either of them to get the
idea he can deal with us the way he's been dealing with
Slick. We might even want to raise prices on the Slick line.
I've got an idea as to how we might maneuver them to
play along, but I want to sleep on it, maybe for several
nights.

G. B. WAITE

TO: Mr. Waite

RE: Phone call from Mr. Gibbons

Mr. Gibbons reported at 3:30 P.M. today that one of
his two large chain-store customers notified him verbally
this afternoon that Slick Appliances will receive no more
orders after the first of next month—i.e., next Wednesday.
Mr. Gibbons says he is expecting the other large customer
will also cancel out in the immediate future unless Slick
is able to promise larger deliveries next fall.

I told Mr. Gibbons the executive committee was going to
take the merger matter up Friday morning, but he was
extremely anxious to discuss this with you personally before
the meeting.

FRED GROSVENOR

FROM THE PRESIDENT'S DESK:

TO:   Mr. Grosvenor

I talked with Gibbons for some time last evening at
my home, and now I've decided to move in on that merger

proposition immediately. Conversations with both of Slick's large customers first thing this morning produced firm agreements that they both would remain Slick customers if we took over Slick and expanded it at once. I have told Gibbons to come over and explain his proposals on the merger to the executive committee at eleven o'clock tomorrow morning.

This move is bound to disturb some members of the committee, and it is frankly not what I had anticipated doing right at this time, as I've already indicated. Since the responsibility for this step is all mine, I don't propose to waste the committee's time with long-winded explanations. As a matter of fact, I probably couldn't explain to the committee logically why I decided to go ahead with this merger right now, in view of my previous doubts about the timing. The pressure put on Slick by its two large customers was not the crucial factor; I still feel we could have won them back to Slick's high-quality product as soon as we could provide the volume they wanted, though keeping them as customers will naturally save us a big lot of money in maintaining break-even operations until we can beef up Slick's plant with new capacity.

However, other factors in this merger seemed just as important to me; for instance, the sizable loss carry-back we'll pick up from Slick will be very useful to us this year. Also, I am now convinced that by merging immediately we'll forestall the loss of Slick's valuable research chief, who is already being wooed, I understand, by several companies. Then there's the benefit of stirring up our own management personnel. In fact, this might turn out to be one of the biggest advantages of the merger, but I won't be going into this with the committee, for various reasons.

This may give you some idea of the complications involved in my arriving at this decision, which I assure you was not a cut-and-dried matter of reasoning and logic. All I can say for certain is that I feel right about the thing, on the basis of my experience and judgment.

G. B. Waite

to: Mr. Waite

re: Message from Mr. Burroughs, sales vice president

After the executive-committee meeting this morning, Mr. Burroughs stopped at my desk and discussed some of the points he had raised against the merger with Slick during the meeting. He is very concerned about your decision, which he interprets as meaning that our company will not be diversifying in non-electrical products, as he has strongly urged. He seemed personally upset, and asked me to arrange an appointment with you as soon as possible. I have scheduled him for 4:45 this afternoon, in your office.

Fred Grosvenor

from the president's desk:

to:    Mr. Grosvenor

My meeting with Tim Burroughs yesterday produced some unfortunate reactions that I did not anticipate. I expected Burroughs to be disappointed about the merger with Slick, but I did not expect him to be so violent about it. He implied he would resign unless I could assure him we would diversify soon in non-electrical products. This didn't seem like Tim at all, and I spent a long time trying to dig out of him what the real trouble was.

It finally turned out that he was afraid I would be bringing in Slick's research chief, a bright chap named Harold Treat, to replace Tim's old crony and brother-in-law, Herb Shipley.

I admitted I was planning to make good use of Treat, in developing new products for us, but I assured Tim I have no intention of sidetracking or dropping an excellent research chief like our Herb Shipley. As a matter of fact, I am tentatively planning to promote Shipley to a new position as vice president of market research. However, I didn't tell Tim this, because I first wanted to see how Herb himself takes to the idea. I managed to calm Tim down by reassuring him that neither he nor Herb has anything to worry about in this merger, and that Slick's man Treat isn't going to displace anyone, etc.

Nevertheless, Tim's reaction forces me to make an early decision about Herb Shipley, which I certainly wish I could postpone for a while. I would like to see Herb in my office on Monday afternoon, providing he's not going to be tied up then. Sometime before then I will want to look through his personal file.

G. B. WAITE

TO: Mr. Waite

RE: Mr. Shipley's personal file

The personnel department informs me that Mr. Shipley's file has apparently been mislaid. While they are searching for this, I will collect copies of the merit ratings on him from the files of his former supervisors, and also the data on promotions and payroll increases from the controller's office.

In addition, I secured from Mr. Shipley's secretary copies of technical articles by him that have been published in various journals; these are attached herewith.

FRED GROSVENOR

FROM THE PRESIDENT'S DESK:

TO:    Mr. Grosvenor

The material you have sent me on Herb Shipley was helpful, and in thinking over his career with us I feel I know it so well that I won't need his complete personal file. His professional record as a metallurgist I knew was outstanding, but the contributions he has made to our manufacturing processes are far more numerous and varied than I had remembered.

However, these things aren't what have been worrying me. What I'd like to know is how Herb would handle the nontechnical problems he'll be facing as head of market research, where he'll be dealing with sales and planning problems as well as product development. A man with his intelligence, background, and training ought to be capable of handling this new position, but I want to be sure that Herb himself thinks so. He's a fine man, and I want to keep him satisfied and productive.

G. B. WAITE

FROM THE PRESIDENT'S DESK:

TO:    Mr. Grosvenor

My talk with Herb Shipley this morning was both reassuring and disturbing. He is a quiet man, as you know, and it was difficult to get him to open up, but when I indicated he was shortly going to be recommended for a vice presidency of market research, Herb seemed genuinely delighted. I was struck more forcibly than ever with Herb's straightforward honesty about himself. He said he didn't know very much about market research, but felt quite capable of learning the subject in a reasonably short time. Then he asked me what his duties would entail, and though I could only give him an approximate picture, he seemed confident he could handle the job.

The disturbing part of my interview with Herb came at the end when I made a remark about his "learning the salesman's game." Herb replied in a joking way that he "couldn't promise any wonders" but that he'd "do the very best he could." I think he spoke the honest truth, and that's why, after he left, I got to thinking about Herb's great sense of responsibility, and compared him with that fellow Borden who finally left us last year. You may remember how Borden always thought he managed to keep out of trouble by avoiding making decisions, or making only those that would please his bosses. Borden became less and less active as a manager, and would let things go until something came up, some incidental factor or accident, and he would let this make the decision for him. In Borden's case, I think his indecision was the result of conflict between his own personal code and the policies of the company.

He had a very logical mind and at first he was always insisting on "getting all the facts," but after two or three decisions by me and the executive committee that seemed unreasonable to Borden, he sort of pulled in his horns and appeared to lose interest in his job. I guess he thought I wasn't very bright when I told him one day that there were a good many times when I distrusted the power of reason and preferred to follow a hunch. The biggest trouble with a fellow like Borden, it seems to me, is that he's afraid to trust any decision he can't back up logically.

However, Herb Shipley has got courage, plus an exceedingly strong sense of responsibility to the company. That's what deeply concerns me now, for when I consider his technical background and training I realize he'll have a terrific time adjusting to the non-technical approaches and ideas of the marketing division. He might become absorbed in a lot of surveys and statistical studies of customers, etc., and lose sight of the job of managing the division. I don't doubt him when he says he's confident he can handle the market-research job; he *is* confident, but that doesn't necessarily mean he'll be able to do the job. What worries me most is that Herb's sense of responsibility to the company might make him drive himself unmercifully trying to do a job that maybe he just isn't competent to handle, no matter how hard he tries. That could crack him up seriously, and even the thought of such a thing happening to a fine man like Herb makes me sweat.

At the same time, Herb is one of our outstanding managers and I propose to stand by my decision to award him the recognition he fully deserves.

G. B. WAITE

TO: Mr. Waite

RE: Mr. Shipley's report on Product Developments

This morning Mr. Shipley left with me the attached report which he prepared on several new techniques he is recommending for the manufacturing division.

FRED GROSVENOR

FROM THE PRESIDENT'S DESK:

TO:     Mr. Grosvenor

You will be interested to hear that I have revised my decision regarding the appointment of Herb Shipley as vice president of market research. This matter has been on my mind for more than a week now, and last night I finally came to the conclusion that I simply could not live with my decision to put him in that position. I am convinced that the risk to him, personally, would be too great, because of his powerful sense of responsibility to the company. Therefore I have been thinking of ways to get around this situation, and have decided on a relatively simple solution. I am going to ask the board to make Herb the vice president of technical development. This is a position that can be defined so as to relieve Herb of any responsibilities regarding market research.

This solution I can directly present to Herb with a clear conscience. I am confident he will accept it willingly, and that the change of title can be rationalized to his satisfaction on the basis of his recent excellent report on product developments. This will not only preserve his self-respect but should also, I think, stimulate him to do an even better job in the field in which he is best qualified.

As I write this I am aware that I have probably made the decisions in this whole matter sound entirely reasonable and logical. I guess that is a common enough habit for anyone who has been raised to admire and respect the results of analytical thinking and "common sense." I can recall how impressed I was as a young man when I first learned the satisfactions of a well-thought-out, logical argument, and subsequently I always admired those who could present things with such precision and completeness that no intelligent person could possibly object to the final conclusions or recommendations. However, I have since learned how deceptive such arguments can be, and how often the appearance of completeness by the use of statistics and diagrams, for instance, missed the real point of a problem, or overlooked some small detail that could—and usually did—change the whole picture.

In this connection, I would commend to your attention the superb description of the virtues of the non-logical approach to decision making that Chester Barnard presented to some Princeton students back in 1936; you will find it included as an appendix to Barnard's well-known book on *The Functions of the Executive.* As Barnard says, "the practical necessities often require chiefly the non-logical processes," and in my thinking about Herb Shipley I know I have relied heavily on my feelings about Herb and on the impressions he has given me about his character. Also, I depend continually on what I can only call my sense of what would be "the right thing to do." I suppose some psychologists would be ready to define and analyze the basis of any of my decisions in terms of my personality, or my subconscious motives, or my cultural background, etc. I don't say these things didn't operate to prejudice me in favor of Herb; but I do not think any analysis of my decisions would ever show exactly how all the various conscious factors and subconscious motives were related—i.e., which were more powerful, which less, and so on.

Strictly speaking, my decision about Herb can't be evaluated for quite a while yet, at least until he's been in the new job long enough for me to see whether he's going to work out, or whether the change was good for Herb. I couldn't tell you now how I'll decide either of these things. It might turn out that Herb will do a fine technical job of developing techniques and improvements that make money for the company; and at the same time he may fail to encourage the younger men in his department to contribute as much as they could, with the result that the company's engineering eventually might acquire a series of traditional and "untouchable" approaches to problems. Of course I hope I would be smart enough to see such a thing, and prevent it, but my high opinion of Herb might make me blind to it, at least for too long a time. At the same time, my opinion of Herb is going to complicate my decision as to whether this new assignment is good for him. Right now I feel sure it is best to confine him to a field where his ability is unquestionable. I still get a nervous feeling when I think what would happen to him if he couldn't really accomplish an assignment for the company.

But what if I'm off the beam? What if I've underestimated his ability, and have taken from Herb an opportunity that could effectively broaden him as a manager? He's only got ten more years before he hits retirement at sixty-five, and in that time it is possible that, if I had decided differently, he could have developed into an outstanding president of the company.

It's things like these that make you realize how terribly important a management decision about a man can be, and how silly it is to assume that "common sense" and reasoning are going to bring you out all right in the end. No matter how much I may explain and describe such decisions for you, you will not know how you are going to decide such matters when you have to. I'm not saying you should throw reason and facts and logic out the window; you have to use these constantly, and try to be always as objective as you can. But you've got to do a lot more than this, too. You're going to have to learn for yourself what good timing is, in making decisions, and how to be either prompt *or* deliberate, as the case seems to indicate. You'll have to be flexible enough so that you can, if necessary, backtrack and change your decision; but at the same time you can't do this so much that you appear to others to be vacillating. You'll have to weigh considerations, such as whether to decide so as to benefit a man's development or so as to benefit the company; and you'll have to take risk courageously, without evasion, no matter how foresighted you may think you're being at the time. Without courage, in fact, you might as well abandon the hope of learning how to be decisive.

Maybe I've said enough by now to show you what I meant when I said earlier that my decision about Herb Shipley can't be judged for quite a while yet. Don't let anyone ever tell you that decision making is merely a matter of getting the facts and reaching a conclusion.

G. B. WAITE

CHAPTER SIX     *Emotional*
                *Stability*

*The capacity for emotional stability has been rec-
ognized for centuries as essential for those who
hope to rule, manage, lead, or otherwise influence
others. For the executive in the modern large corporation this capacity may become so crucially important that an emotional outburst can sabotage
his career, or it can reveal to his superiors that he
is in fact a relatively mature manager. The functioning of an executive's emotions follows no ster-
eotyped pattern, and the ability to identify stability
in a manager requires a first-hand knowledge of
psychological processes that few executives can be
expected to acquire. But the intelligent executive
who has himself well under control may better
grasp the nature of stability than the professional
psychologist who has little more than an intellec-
tual knowledge of such phenomena.*

*In this chapter, various and common kinds of
emotional stability and instability are presented
through the personalities of a corporation president, his personnel director, and two of his other
top men.*

Harold Norris read the memorandum again, and again he felt more uneasy than he could remember having felt in his nine years as personnel director of Chemway Corp. Why was McGinnis dropping this in his lap, anyway? He picked up a paper clip, bent it savagely, and threw it hard against the door of his small office. He sat there for a moment, then suddenly picked up the memorandum again and read it for the third time.

CONFIDENTIAL

TO:    Mr. H. E. Norris, Personnel Director

Dear Hal:

Wish I didn't have to bother you with this, but I guess I'll just have to, now, after what happened yesterday afternoon. I'm sure you know what the trouble is, since you probably heard about it at once from Ted Frawley himself, but my version may be somewhat different. As I got it from Ben Pierce, Ted returned from lunch yesterday and started to quarrel with Jerry Walsh, his top salesman, about sales quotas for next quarter. They both got very mad, Ben says, and when Jerry called Ted some kind of a dirty name, Ted exploded, and fired Jerry. According to Ben, Jerry assumed Ted would cool off overnight, but when Ted was still sore this morning, Jerry handed in his resignation effective as soon as a replacement can be found.

I can't understand how Ted ever got himself into a jam like this, for he knows how much the company needs Jerry's sales talents, especially these days with those foreign companies breathing down our necks. But Ted lost control all right, and now I want you to see what you can do to get things back to normal. Maybe you can have a long lunch with Ted and persuade him of the error of his ways. If he will apologize to Jerry, I'm sure this unfortunate event can be smoothed over and the two men can be put back into working order again.

Let me know, Hal, if there's anything I can do to help. And best of luck to you in this matter.

CHARLES O. McGINNIS

Norris sighed as he finished reading. He knew that Mc-Ginnis was not the kind of president who would expect to be asked for help in handling this affair. No matter how many times McGinnis might offer to help, he was never one to get mixed up in these personal problems. Whenever something unpleasant happened, McGinnis would always minimize it; he would try to laugh it off, and would always manage to say something optimistic. Norris had long since learned that the more optimistic McGinnis sounded about something, the gloomier the thing was likely to be. But now Norris felt that in this case McGinnis really thought this blowup between Frawley and Walsh could be patched up without much trouble. Norris believed otherwise; in fact, he considered the two men natural enemies, and in his opinion this fight had simply brought their feelings about each other out into public view. That meant it was possible that he, Norris, was being asked by McGinnis to accomplish something that was next to impossible.

The thought made him wonder suspiciously if McGinnis was really putting him on a spot the way he had lately put the controller, Ben Pierce, on the spot by asking for long-range ten-year forecasts. Norris could feel his anger rising as his suspicion of McGinnis' motives grew stronger, and he had the impulse to tell McGinnis to handle Frawley and Walsh himself. But the impulse faded almost immediately, for he knew he wouldn't dare jeopardize his standing with

McGinnis in this way. Yet he was determined to avoid getting mixed up in this personnel mess, if there was any reasonable way he could do so, and almost as soon as he began to think of his problem from this viewpoint, the solution came to him. He decided to call in a psychological consultant and turn the whole business over to him. The idea pleased Norris, and he was sure McGinnis would approve, even though he knew McGinnis was inclined to be leery of psychologists.

Norris picked up his phone and asked his secretary to call a friend of his at one of the major management-consulting firms. A few minutes later Norris got from him the name of Rolfe Bolling, a clinical psychologist who, his friend thought, could do a good job with Frawley and Walsh. Half an hour later, Norris located Bolling at a Chicago hotel where he was conferring with a client. Though Bolling seemed hesitant at first to take on the job, Norris persuaded him by offering to have Chemway's private plane pick him up the next day and bring him over to Cleveland to have "a look at the situation."

A week later Norris received this letter from psychologist Bolling:

Dear Mr. Norris:

I am sorry I haven't let you know sooner about my interesting experiences at Chemway last week, but my other commitments have prevented me from doing so until now. As it is, I can only send you a preliminary brief report, for when I replayed the tape recordings of my interviews with some of your executives, I found several things that indicate I was premature in saying to you last Friday that the personal problems of Mr. Frawley and Mr. Walsh might be solved rather quickly.

What Mr. Frawley's trouble is I would not, of course, be in a position to say without spending an extensive amount of

time with him and his associates. On the other hand, I think
Mr. Walsh's troubles are relatively minor and superficial, and
could be helped to disappear as a result of the therapy that
Mr. Frawley might be induced to undertake.

These preliminary findings may involve far more extensive
consultation than you anticipated when you asked me to
visit your company. It may surprise you if I say that in my
present opinion a good many of the difficulties you are experi-
encing with emotional displays have originated in the personalities of some of the people in your company who are
undoubtedly considered entirely "normal" and emotionally
stable. There is at least one marked case of obsessive-compul-
sive behavior, which seems potentially very disruptive, and
there is also a clear case of what we call "hysteroid" behavior,
which I believe is causing considerable maladjustment in
this man's associates. Both of these cases would require at
least as much study as the case of Mr. Frawley.

However, I wish to make it clear that you would be under
no obligation to undertake any therapy that I might consider
necessary.

In any case, it was a pleasure to meet you, and I want to
thank you again for the consideration you showed me in
arranging for my transportation by plane to your company
last week.

Sincerely,
ROLFE BOLLING

Norris let the letter drop on his desk. This was not quite
what he had bargained for, and he felt annoyed at Bolling,
who, he suspected, was trying to induce Chemway Corp. to
become one of his major clients. But Norris didn't intend to
back out now, particularly since Bolling's references to other
Chemway executives in need of counseling had not only
aroused his curiosity but had suddenly given him the idea

that, as Bolling's sponsor, he might win some real recognition from his associates. He himself didn't care much for psychologists, actually, but he decided that from now on he wasn't going to let Bolling and his psychological jargon irritate him. And he wasn't going to worry about the expense, either. After all, he told himself, it was his responsibility as personnel director to use the best techniques he could find to keep Chemway Corp.'s top management in good working order. This sense of responsibility made him feel very confident, and within the next fifteen minutes he had dictated a graceful reply to Bolling, praising the sharpness of his observations and inviting him to "come to Chemway as soon as possible and do whatever is best for the company's executives."

When Norris signed the letter to Bolling later that afternoon, he felt greatly relieved, as though he had finally found the one man who could be trusted to solve his problem. He did not even worry about having to explain to Frawley and Walsh why Bolling was coming to talk to them and others in the company; Norris decided he would simply say Bolling was making a study of Chemway's executives in order to revise the company's management appraisal forms.

After Bolling arrived the following week, and had begun to interview intensively not only Frawley and Walsh, but also Ben Pierce and two or three of his subordinates, Norris became more and more relaxed and cheerful. He took Bolling to lunch every day during the first week, and discovered that Bolling would say practically nothing about the other men in the company he was talking with. This increased Norris' respect for Bolling, and one day he found himself confiding to Bolling the fact that he secretly felt he shouldn't have bought the big house his wife had recently persuaded him to buy. Norris said he thought the house was too extravagant for someone whose job involved, as his did, the winning of local public good will for the company; but his wife had told him he had to live up to the appearances people expected of one of the company's high-level executives. "I finally gave in to her," Norris told Bolling, "but I'm still afraid I made a mistake." But when Bolling merely smiled and said nothing, Norris became uneasy, and quickly changed the subject. After that, he didn't talk with Bolling much, and the few times he did he merely gave his impressions of certain people Bolling asked him about.

When Bolling left the plant after about four weeks of interviewing, Norris was relieved to see him go, and at the same time somewhat anxious about the report he expected to get from the consultant. He became more worried as the days passed, and by the time he received Bolling's report he was definitely on edge. He forced himself to read the report slowly:

Dear Mr. Norris:

I hope you have not been inconvenienced by my delay in sending you this report on certain executives in your company. The fact of the matter is that I have had a rather more difficult time analyzing the situations and people involved than I had expected to, and there were times when I thought I would certainly have to return to Chemway Corp. for further investigations. However, I decided that this was not actually necessary at this stage. A preliminary report will provide you with information that will indicate the broad nature of the problems on which you may wish to take action in the very near future. Consequently, I am going to make this report more informal than might normally be the case, with the understanding, of course, that you will advise me as to any points or further details that you may wish in connection with my studies of these men and their difficulties.

I think it will be best for me to submit this report in two

major sections, the first dealing with the difficulties of Mr.
Theodore Frawley and Mr. Gerald Walsh; the second sec-
tion, to follow later, will deal with the men whose problems
I found closely related to those of others in the company.

*The Frawley-Walsh Difficulty.* The following facts were
collected concerning the recent clash between Mr. Theodore
Frawley, sales vice president, and Mr. Gerald Walsh, district
sales manager. This event took place on Wednesday afternoon, January 19, shortly after Frawley had returned to his
office following a long lunch hour spent at the Athletic Club.
Frawley had been drinking rather heavily; a waiter at the
club said he had served Frawley three martinis before lunch
and two double Scotches after lunch while Frawley played
several games of "twenty-one" in the grill room. Up to last
fall, the waiter said, Frawley sometimes drank nothing at all
while lunching at the club, but since about mid-October he
had imbibed generously every single day. The waiter said
Frawley was never noisy or objectionable no matter how
much he drank; but he often seemed depressed and after
lunch would sit alone just looking out the window at the
traffic.

The waiter could not recall anything that was especially
different about Frawley's conduct during last January. However, Frawley's secretary, Miss Thompson, told me that on
the morning of the nineteenth, Frawley had spent over an
hour in Mr. McGinnis' office; presumably they were discussing a bothersome sales problem in the New England territory, for Frawley had asked Miss Thompson for the file on
this matter before going to see McGinnis. I have examined
this file and found it deals chiefly with the sharp drop in
sales in the Boston area, apparently caused by competition
from a lower-priced line of chemicals introduced by a foreign competitor. But I saw some pencil notations, "see Walsh
re this," on the margin of one of the sales sheets, and asked

Miss Thompson if she could explain it. She then told me that Walsh was a Boston-born Irishman, had formerly been a salesman in the Boston area, and had more than once "kidded" Frawley about the approach he was using toward Boston jobbers. She said Walsh thought Frawley ought to stop trying to impress the jobbers with a "high-sounding institutional pitch," and start selling them by doing them small favors, and using other similar methods of personal salesmanship. Frawley strongly disagreed, Miss Thompson said, and insisted that Chemway ought to stick to institutional advertising and "dignified" sales methods.

I have since checked Miss Thompson's statements with both Frawley and Walsh and what she told me is substantially correct. She also commented on the drastic change in Frawley's manner since last fall. He used to personify his nickname, "Tireless Ted," and would go at full speed all day long, she said; he also spent a great many evenings entertaining important out-of-town customers. His weekends at his New Jersey home were usually very social, filled with golf dates, bridge parties, cocktail parties, etc., etc. But since October she said she was sure he had only occasionally engaged in this kind of activity. On Monday mornings now he would often complain privately to her about some "stupid affair" he had attended over the weekend; whereas she said he used to go around the office grinning and chuckling about something he had heard or seen during the weekend. She said he had been "always cheerful" but now he was "terribly gloomy."

This picture of the marked change in Frawley's demeanor is presented to show you how his psychological problems have affected his behavior in and out of the office since last October. This alone should be sufficient to convince you that Frawley's outburst against Walsh was no mere temporary symptom, but the sign of a serious shift in his personality.

Without any more evidence, I would have been ready to identify Frawley as a clear case of emotional instability; but this fact does not tell us why, or what might be done to help him recover his earlier effectiveness. The answers to these questions were forthcoming from the results of the series of interviews I had with Frawley. I will try to keep my report on these interviews as brief and as nontechnical as possible.

The first interview was, as I expected, not too productive. Frawley was naturally suspicious of me and my motives. He responded apathetically to questions about his early family life and boyhood experiences, and showed irritation whenever I pressed for more details. I early noted he had a habit of scratching his underarm when questioned about his personal life, which I thought was symptomatic of some psychological conversion on his part. In the second interview Frawley opened up, however. The information he gave me about his parents and his two brothers was commonplace, but informative, i.e., an easygoing father and a serious, often stern mother who was ambitious for all her sons, but apparently most ambitious for the youngest, who was Theodore. Frawley often was ridiculed by his older brothers as "mother's pet," and he most resented his oldest brother who mimicked the mother and called him "Teddy boy."

The mother, however, apparently never showed much real affection for any of the boys; instead, she kept urging them to "be good and make good." When they misbehaved, she would often lament that she had not had any daughters. The father took no interest in disciplining the boys, but would often amuse them by singing Irish songs in his light tenor voice; he never became more than a clerk in the local telephone company.

Later interviews with Frawley brought out revealing connections between these points and his attitudes toward Jerry Walsh. As Frawley became more talkative about himself he admitted that he had disliked Walsh for years but had been careful not to show it, hiding his feelings behind his usual buoyant and boyish manner. Sometimes, Frawley confessed, he had become violently angry at Walsh and "his easygoing ways," especially the way he could shrug off the loss of a big order. When I pressed Frawley on this point, he suddenly blurted out that he "didn't even like the sound of Walsh's voice!"—and then he almost immediately realized why: Walsh had the same high tenor voice his father had had, and in addition Walsh strongly resembled Frawley's older brother.

After this disclosure, it wasn't too long before I had helped him to see that his dislike of Walsh, like his dislike of his father and older brother, had been the product of childhood rejection, not by his father and brother, but by his mother. The mother had refused her sons the love they craved from her, and Frawley, unable to admit this rejection to himself, had repressed it in his subconscious. The subconscious anger he felt toward his mother had been directed toward his father and older brother. Frawley did not express this anger openly; he was strongly inhibited from such action by the impact of his mother's repeated injunction to "be good and make good." In addition, I helped Frawley see that his mother's injunction had established in him a great fear of failure.

It was this fear of failure that eventually overpowered Frawley last October. He had always driven himself to succeed in whatever he did, and he had nearly always succeeded, mainly because he had a way of pleasing and persuading people. He had, for example, long ago convinced President McGinnis that he was "the best damn sales vice president in the country." But by last October, Frawley's new sales program for Chemway Corp., which he had personally worked out for meeting the threat of foreign com-

petitors, had turned out to be a dismal flop; Chemway's
share of Eastern markets had actually fallen off by 15 per
cent during the sales campaign, whereas Frawley had opti-
mistically pledged before McGinnis and the entire sales force
that his program would "put us at least 25 per cent ahead of
those foreigners." The failure of his program was the biggest
Frawley had ever experienced, and, after unsuccessful efforts
to rationalize it in one way or another, he told me he at first
had concluded that he was not merely "a lousy sales manager" but was also a "loudmouthed bastard with big ideas."

After that, he said, he began to realize that all his life he
had been driving himself because he was afraid of being a
failure. His ambition to "make good" appeared to him to be
a "cheap thing" that his mother had instilled in him; and the
things he'd been chasing—a big salary, fame as a sales wizard,
and the acclaim of his associates—now looked "cheap" to
him, too. This reversal in his attitudes toward himself and
toward his objectives and social values hit him with terrific
force; it was so insulting to the picture he had previously had
of himself that he lost all respect for himself. The results
were plainly visible in his morose behavior, his heavy drinking, his extreme irritability and suspiciousness.

It was not therefore at all surprising that Frawley blew his
top at his best salesman, Jerry Walsh. When Walsh came
over to Frawley after lunch that day and suggested making
a trip to Boston to "see some friends of his about Chemway's
line," Frawley was, first, consciously angered; he suspected
Walsh of wanting to apply his personal sales tactics in
Boston, and thus show that Frawley's sales approach had
been wrong. But Frawley also immediately reacted subcon-
sciously and explosively. Walsh reminded Frawley subcon-
sciously of his older brother who had teased him so, and this
roused the long-repressed anger he had felt toward his
mother. No longer now able to suppress this great anger

(because of the drastic shift that had occurred in his personality), Frawley began to seethe, and when Walsh went on to tell him he really thought Frawley's sales program might "make good" in the Boston area, the valve on Frawley's anger blew wide open. Frawley turned on Walsh the resentment he had been storing up for years; he bellowed at Walsh to "shut up and get the hell out of here." Walsh was astonished, and in trying to calm Frawley, he unwittingly made the mistake of referring to Frawley's program as "the pet project" of McGinnis, which it was. But to Frawley, the word "pet" instantly recalled all those times he had been accused of being his mother's pet, and this maddened him to the point of striking the hardest blow he could at Walsh, i.e., he fired him.

I won't prolong this report much longer, but I do want to add one or two things. You can see that Frawley is not well, and will need some psychiatric treatment; I would recommend that he be sent for a checkup to some clinic where he can rest and be helped to get himself in perspective, and so regain his self-respect. One place I know of will give him a thorough going-over, a physical and emotional analysis resulting in diagnosis and recommendations in a period of only seven days; however, you may wish him to take an extended leave of absence under professional care, which would probably ensure his full recovery.

I trust the foregoing is sufficiently self-explanatory. Please do not hesitate to ask for further clarification of any points set forth. You realize, I am sure, that emotional instability such as Frawley has exhibited is no simple matter. There are many more details that might be included, but I have purposely omitted these in the interests of getting across the essentials.

Respectfully yours,
Rolfe Bolling

When Norris finished Bolling's report, he felt grateful for what Bolling had sent him, yet he also felt slightly resentful that an outsider like Bolling should have said all the things he said about his good friend Frawley. It didn't seem decent to Norris, and he decided he would not show McGinnis the psychologist's report, but would summarize it for him in a confidential conference. McGinnis, he was sure, would never wade through Bolling's extended descriptions, anyway; what McGinnis would want would be a quick and simple explanation with "a positive ending." Norris believed he could supply this without much trouble; but he first planned to let McGinnis read at least one or two of Bolling's comments, so that McGinnis would appreciate the ability that he, Norris, had shown in boiling the reports down to what McGinnis called "the essence." Norris imagined himself telling McGinnis, "These psychologist ginks are peculiar, C. O., and what they really mean is . . . "

But Norris continued to feel uneasy about Bolling's investigation and he decided he would rather discuss privately with Bolling what the psychologist said he had discovered about other executives in the company. Besides, in a talk with Bolling, he could ask some of the questions that were on his mind as a result of Bolling's report. Norris called his secretary in and dictated a short note to Bolling suggesting that Bolling present part two of his report on Chemway's executives in person.

Bolling arrived at Norris' office about a week later and Norris found himself greeting him stiffly as though there had been some unpleasantness between them. Bolling, however, seemed relaxed and came right to the point with his first question. "Have there been any further developments in the Frawley situation?" he asked. "I thought that something might have happened when I received your note about coming here to have a face-to-face talk with you."

Norris shook his head. "No, Dr. Bolling, things are about the same as when you left, and that's one reason I thought we could discuss whatever steps you think ought to be taken about Frawley. I think your idea of sending him to that clinic you mentioned makes sense."

"Have you approached Frawley yet?" Bolling asked. "You know he may not take to the idea at all."

"No, I haven't said anything to anybody since getting your report, but I assumed Ted would go along with a suggestion that he take a rest and go through some kind of emotional checkup, and I'd appreciate having your advice on how to broach the matter to him."

"Well, if I were you, I'd let Mr. McGinnis make the suggestion," Bolling said. "He's Frawley's direct boss, and would probably have much more effect on Frawley than you would. I assume Mr. McGinnis has seen my report?"

Norris was embarrassed by Bolling's question, but tried to sound casual as he replied, "Well, as a matter of fact he hasn't. I didn't want to show it to him until I had had a chance to talk with you."

Bolling looked sharply at Norris and made no immediate reply. There was an awkward silence, and Norris offered Bolling a cigarette, which Bolling took. Bolling thought he knew why Norris had kept the report from McGinnis, and he decided to check his hunch. "I'm glad in a way that you haven't talked to McGinnis yet," he said, "because there are a couple of important comments I'd like to make on the whole subject of Chemway's problems as I see them now. One matter concerns Mr. Benson Pierce, your controller. I think you ought to know that he's almost as unstable as Frawley is."

Norris, startled, sat forward in his chair. "Ben Pierce unstable? You can't mean that! Why, around here, we consider him about the most hardheaded and practical man in the office. When it comes to checking on figures, especially expense accounts, Ben's as icy as a deep freeze."

Bolling smiled. "I know he probably strikes you that way, but in the talks I had with him he showed himself up as an introverted type with a compulsion neurosis. This kind of neurosis is fairly common among accountants, and some of it shows up in their strictness with subordinates about accuracy and neatness. In addition, Pierce's compulsion leads him to be constantly grooming his nails and hands, and I learned that he washes his hands as many as eight or ten times during a single office day. He's probably struggling with some subconscious guilt feeling, which, of course, may be nothing more than some forbidden adolescent act that he's suppressed into his subconscious."

"But he still does a damn good job of work," Norris retorted.

"Yes," Bolling replied. "I'm not worried about his guilt feelings really. What concerns me is his growing suspicion of other people, especially of McGinnis, who Pierce says is out to get him. When I asked Pierce what proof he had of this, he mentioned only those requests for long-range forecasts, which you had already told me about. Pierce says he doesn't know much about forecasting, and he's sure McGinnis is aiming to replace him or kick him upstairs into some advisory position. Pierce is really on edge."

"I'll be damned," Norris said. "I'd never have suspected it. He certainly hasn't shown any signs of strain."

"He's showing them all right," Bolling said. "He's taking tranquilizers now and has taken to working late so he can postpone the irritating contacts he nearly always now has with his wife. Seems he and his wife have fallen out over some local amateur theatre group; Pierce thinks she's trying to be arty and that she is stubbornly keeping it up just to embarrass him."

"Can't say as I blame him much," Norris said. "You can't condemn a man simply because he's got marital problems, can you?"

"Of course not," Bolling replied, "but it's just one more thing that's wearing him raw. Another thing is McGinnis' insistence that all Chemway's managers take part in local community affairs. Pierce says he just won't be pushed around. His compulsiveness, however, comes out indirectly in the way he obstructs McGinnis' policies. For example, I learned from Frawley, for one, that Pierce is strictly enforcing some old accounting routines and regulations that make it very hard for some of the other managers to justify any expenditures they might have made for drinks and entertainment, for instance, in attempting to advance the company's community relations. Obviously, this is Pierce's little revenge on McGinnis."

Norris was growing impatient at Bolling's professional assumptions. "Well, what do you propose we do about Ben? You can't prosecute a man just because he resents some company policy."

"Unfortunately, about the only effective step you could take is out of the question," Bolling said.

"What's that?" Norris asked.

Bolling smiled. "Get a new president, and I'm not joking," he answered. "Get an emotionally stable president."

Norris started to laugh, but stopped as suddenly as he'd begun. He saw that Bolling was serious. "Now look here, Bolling," he said, "how can you say that McGinnis is emotionally unstable? He's one of the most cheerful, pleasant-mannered men I've ever met. I've never seen him really angry with anybody."

"That's just it. He never does get angry, according to everyone I've talked to here. McGinnis is what we psychologists call a 'hysteroid' type, and among his symptoms are a confirmed optimism, a bland unwillingness to face unpleasant realities, and a tendency to think in vague, indecisive terms. The danger is that McGinnis' kind of personality runs the risk of cracking up under an adverse situation it can't evade or get around somehow. What is worse, an extreme hysteroid type usually allows weaknesses in the organization to go uncorrected, and will adopt stopgap measures rather than use any drastic cures. For example, Frawley tells me McGinnis has for a long time recognized that the company should have expert market analyses and forecasts; but McGinnis refuses to recognize that Pierce really isn't capable of providing such data. Instead of facing up to the issue by removing Pierce and getting in someone who can give the company what it needs, McGinnis goes along with Pierce's incapacity and keeps hopefully asking him for long-range forecasts. It looks to me as though McGinnis might come smack up against a real marketing crisis one of these days that will be largely of his own making."

Norris felt that he ought to defend McGinnis, but he didn't know how. Bolling's observations, he conceded, seemed to make sense, and gave Norris an odd feeling of satisfaction. After a moment's pause, he expressed the only protest he thought Bolling might accept. "Well, I don't know about McGinnis' psychological problems," he said, "but I do know we can't expect to do anything about them. He's one of those bosses who don't take kindly to you psychology fellows."

"I know," Bolling said. "His type rarely does—and I'm not suggesting you try to sell him on us, either. That's why I said you'd have to get a new president if you wanted to relieve Pierce's troubles. But I hope at least by now I've helped you get a clearer idea about some of the personal complications that your top brass is suffering from. Actually, I've only touched on a few of the things that might be involved in the cases of Pierce and McGinnis and, for that matter, in Frawley's case, too. Believe me, I'm not trying to convince you that I've got these men all figured out, or that your company should undertake a program of psychological counseling for its top men. Some psychologists might urge such a program on you, and they could end up doing a lot of good, too. But this counseling of managers is in my opinion the most delicate operation that can be performed on management, even under the most sympathetic conditions. And if, as in your company's case, the top men are hostile to the idea, you might as well forget about psychological counseling as long as they're around. At any rate, I'm satisfied that my work here ought to help you get Frawley back on the track with some rest and therapy; and I believe our discussions have been worth while, even if they've done no more than show you how instability in one manager can expose the same failing in another. Someday I hope you also have a chance to study how a highly stable manager can encourage stability in his associates."

"I'd like that, for sure," Norris said. He was greatly relieved by what Bolling had said, and wanted him to go on talking. But Bolling suddenly stood up and held his hand out. "Now I've got to get out of here before you ask me what an emotionally stable manager is like." Norris grinned and shook Bolling's hand, and then said, earnestly, "I assure you I'd like to hear what you have to say on that subject. I confess I'm still mixed up about this stability business, the way you've described it."

"Don't let it worry you," Bolling said. "A lot of people are mixed up about it. It's a very complicated business, in fact just as complicated as the big subject of maturity. Go ask your friends what a mature person is, or has, and see how many different answers and prescriptions you get. But for practical purposes, about the best thing you can do is keep your eyes open and figure it out by yourself. In the end, isn't that what everybody has to do for himself, in one degree or another?"

Bolling picked up his hat, and Norris saw that he was smiling slightly as they shook hands and said goodbye.

After Bolling had left, Norris sat quietly in his office for a long time, his mind going back again and again to the pictures of Frawley, Pierce, and McGinnis that he had formed while listening to Bolling's analysis of the men. He saw Frawley as a dejected figure, who was hiding his fear of being a failure; he saw Pierce as a prim, suspicious person who was hiding his fear of authority; and he saw McGinnis as a grinning optimist who was hiding his fear of facing unpleasant facts. Norris realized this was probably too simple to be right, but that's what it all boiled down to, now, as far as he was concerned. Then he at once thought of his own situation, and concluded he was also suffering from fear, and mainly from fear of not being accepted by others—at any rate, that now seemed to be what he was most afraid of. But he guessed that Bolling would say it was some different kind of fear, or maybe several fears.

Norris here perceived something that hadn't occurred to him before: everybody was undoubtedly afraid in one way or another, and the more a person tried to run away from his fears the stronger these fears became, and the more they upset all one's other feelings. The more Norris thought about this, the truer it seemed. He realized, for instance, that whenever he felt guilty about the new house his wife had persuaded him to buy, he also felt irritable about other things. He usually felt better after he had told himself that the company, having given him more authority and a better position, expected him to increase his standard of living. He had for some time known that he was not going to risk future promotions by making the mistake of fraternizing with his former buddies in the company who were making no effort to get ahead. In the end, he told himself, it came down mostly to one thing, and that was having the courage to stick to one's ambitions, and keep working hard to get them, no matter how much other people and situations upset you. That was the kind of stability it took, he thought, and he began to recall some of the experiences that had upset him fairly regularly.

There was the sharp frustration he continued to feel about his status in the company; he would feel this most whenever he found out he was left out of an operations conference that McGinnis had held with his vice presidents, and afterward in the officers' dining room he would have to listen awkwardly to discussions about things that had been taken up at the conference. His frustration at this treatment never disappeared, but he managed to bear it without showing his resentment. He had also found he could manage to recover quickly after a sharp setback from McGinnis or some other officer, such as the time when McGinnis suddenly announced he was cutting in half the budget for management training that Norris had spent weeks preparing. That time, Norris remembered, he had actually managed to laugh at his own predicament, even though it continued to sting him severely. In somewhat the same way, he had managed to ride over the anger he felt toward Ben Pierce, who always thought it was funny to refer to Norris' department as "the personal bureau." Because the other officers had laughed at this the first few times, Pierce kept on using the phrase, but Norris now could ignore it, and he was glad he had been able to stop himself from making cracks about Pierce's department. Fortunately, he told himself, he could usually be objective about the facts of a situation, and he certainly didn't miss the fact that Pierce, as the controller whom McGinnis admired for his "sound" judgment, was in a position to hurt his case by criticizing the expenditures of the personnel department.

That was why, Norris recalled, he had decided not to recommend the use of psychological tests in Chemway Corp. He himself favored the use of tests in some instances, but he was objective enough to see that McGinnis, Pierce, and most of the other top managers would probably favor using such tests on the rank-and-file employees, but would strenuously oppose using them in selecting managers and deciding on promotions. His ability to control his desire to introduce psychological tests, Norris saw, was not merely a matter of objectivity; he also felt very confident about his judgment in introducing other appraisal methods for selecting personnel. He trusted his own understanding of the people at Chemway Corp. This much self-confidence and understanding of others, he was convinced, enabled him to remain undisturbed by top management's opposition to psychological testing. Norris also was sure that his understanding of others —and to some degree his self-confidence—derived from his own attitude toward other people: he was, after all, really sympathetic toward other people and wanted to help them if he could. He thought he could usually appreciate their limitations, and could understand the differences in their views. He felt he could do this not just intellectually, but emotionally; he was able in most cases to get a sense of how the other person was feeling in a situation, that is, he thought he had what Bolling would probably have called "empathy."

This was one kind of feeling, Norris reflected, that seemed to be of considerable help in controlling his other feelings. Yet he knew from his own experience that it wasn't always useful to control his feelings. There were often times when a good bawling out would do a lot of good, both for the person bawled out and the one letting off steam. In fact, Norris knew some managers who could yell at other people pretty often, and yet manage to retain their cooperation and respect. The difference, he thought, was that such people didn't get personal in their criticisms; they managed to convince their subordinates by their everyday conduct that they were sincerely interested only in getting the job done right, and not in venting their feelings on other people. Norris thought that perhaps the best test he knew of as to whether a manager was emotionally stable or not was to check on the reactions of those who had been on the receiving end of a manager's criticisms. If their reaction was resentment or bitterness or anger, then he would conclude that the manager himself was venting similar hard feelings for his own personal reasons. Such a manager was not, in his opinion, what some would call emotionally mature.

Norris recalled that this kind of personal outburst was exactly what Chemway's Ted Frawley had exhibited in his clash with Walsh. He also thought that Ben Pierce's sharp cracks about others showed the same kind of emotional immaturity. But the idea of being mature in one's emotions still seemed odd to Norris. He guessed that it might be impossible for anyone ever to be actually stable or mature emotionally. The feelings were too volatile for that, he thought; perhaps the best one could hope for was a kind of relative stability. This now seemed to him to be something like a delicate balance between self-assertion and consideration for others. It obviously took courage to express your real feelings before others, whereas it wasn't courage but fear or bitterness that made you make personal remarks about others. Likewise, he thought, consideration for others could be based in respect and a desire to be helpful; or it could be based in a gummy kind of sympathy and do-goodism that did nobody any good. The problem of striking a balance between courage and consideration certainly wasn't simple. A man might look brave in expressing a bold conviction to his boss, but actually be doing this only because he privately resented the boss's indifferent attitude toward him. And the same man might appear—even to himself—to be considerate in refraining from criticism of another's idea, yet actually be doing this because he didn't want to offend a person who could hurt his chances for promotion in the company.

As he pondered these complications, Norris realized that in his experience he had run across very few managers who could be said to have even begun to develop a delicate balance between consideration and courageous assertion. He thought one reason for this was that most managers continued to be absorbed primarily in their own feelings and their own careers. Only the exceptional manager seemed capable of the kind of introspection and courage that would allow him to express his feelings in a mature way. Norris wondered if he himself had this kind of maturity, and he was honest enough to doubt that he had. But he thought he had from time to time at least begun to show some of the courage and consideration that emotional maturity required. At such times, it seemed to him, he was more aware of his own responsibility for himself—not only his responsibility for the thoughts and feelings he expressed to others, but also a much tougher kind of responsibility—the full responsibility for those thoughts and feelings he had that others didn't see or hear or otherwise discern, but that were continually active in his own private subjective world. It occurred to Norris that anyone who could maintain *this* kind of responsibility for himself would be about as emotionally stable as a human being could expect to be.

**CHAPTER SEVEN** *Getting Along with People*

*No doctrine of management seems to be so widely accepted as the belief that the secret of executive success today is the ability to "get along with people." This idea is certainly logical: since an executive has to get things done through others, his success will necessarily depend on his skill in influencing others to do what is required. This idea, however, has been so expanded in recent years by sociologists, psychologists, and other students of management that it embraces an astonishing variety of techniques and philosophies. There is perhaps now no error an executive may commit that cannot be somehow attributed to a failure in human relations. Lately, a reaction has set in, and some management students have attacked the overemphasis on human relations in business. But the conscious concern with such relations is here to stay, for it represents a correction of the old abusive carelessness of authoritarian management. The problem now is how to recognize and develop really good relations in industry.*

*In this chapter, that complex of traits involved in "getting along with people" is presented through*

*the imaginary diary of an executive recruiter in a
management-consultant firm. For purposes of clarity, his notes are much more detailed and fluent
than those a real-life recruiter might keep.*

**Tuesday, April 15**

When our new client, President Clyde Regan of American
Toggle Corp., phoned this afternoon and asked me to find
him a new division production manager, the assignment
didn't sound too hard at first; but I've learned that first impressions of such jobs can be deceptive. Regan started out
by telling me he wants an executive who can replace a man
named O'Rourke, who is leaving to accept a vice presidency
at Monometals Inc. Regan made perfectly clear that one
quality was absolutely essential for the replacement: "He's
got to be *really* good with people." Regan is apparently smart
enough to know that's no small order, for he began right
away to spell out for me just what he meant by this phrase.

I soon saw I would have to do considerable reading between the lines, because although Regan uses all the clichés
he is obviously no fool on the subject of "human relations."
He began by commenting on some common ideas about this
business of being *"really* good with people." He said he accepts what he calls "the major ideas about human relations"
in business, and he talked of several: e.g., the fact that management should rely primarily on "persuasion" and not on
"coercion and money rewards" to get workers to work
efficiently; that "workers want to feel secure in their jobs,"
want to be "recognized" by management, and "want to participate in making decisions about their work." Regan also
said that "the techniques of 'communication' are a must at
all levels of management," and it is one of the major respon-

sibilities of executives to "develop the right climate for cooperation" between labor and management. He approves of "group dynamics" and "a clinical approach to leadership."

Having said this, Regan was just as quick to assure me that he doesn't accept any "pat answers or formulas"; said he'd "learned better" at Harvard's advanced management school and he isn't, for instance, looking for a man who believes in that old saw about the "open door"; in his opinion, employees won't ever really feel free to walk in on the boss with their troubles and any boss who thinks otherwise is "living in a dream world." Regan described as equally nonsensical the notion that a manager skilled in human relations can "walk through the shop and call everybody by their first names." He thinks his best division managers rarely get out onto the shop floor, and "never pretend to know a lot of workers' names."

Regan interrupted himself at this point to suggest we continue this discussion in his office tomorrow at nine-thirty. I plan then to pin him down to specific examples of the kind of "human relations" he considers "really good."

**Wednesday, April 16**

Regan greeted me cheerily as I entered the anteroom to his office this morning, and escorted me into his comfortable sanctum. He is a short, energetic man, a bit on the plump side, and very nattily tailored. He wasted no time getting to my business with him. Said he'd been thinking of some other points about human-relations techniques, and had recalled how, before he "learned better," he had manipulated cliques in the company. "Saved me hours of squabbling in a committee room," Regan said.

Nowadays, Regan says, he tries to be more aware of people's feelings and comforts; and if he spotted trivial annoyances in the shop or offices, he would get them removed as soon as possible. As a "small but typical example," Regan said there was the time he noticed that the food-dispensing machines in the office had been empty for a considerable period of time, and he personally phoned the vendor and told him to take the machines out if he couldn't keep them filled up. Regan added that in his opinion one of the best signs that a manager is "really good with people" is that he is always ready to admit his mistakes.

At this point I sensed that stubborn people irritated Regan and thought it would be fruitful to press him later about his memories of the ways in which others had irritated him. But first I switched my line by asking him what sort of responsibilities O'Rourke's successor would have, and Regan quickly filled me in on the production manager's job. Nothing very unusual, it turns out: planning, scheduling, quality control, etc.—plus a strong emphasis on labor relations; shop crew of three superintendents, twenty foremen, and 540 employees, of whom only about fifty were unskilled. Regan emphasized the point that his company has a "good climate of teamwork." However, complications appeared when I asked what he thought would be the toughest problem O'Rourke's successor would face.

Regan frowned slightly, and said the new man would get most of his headaches from dealing with American Toggle's manufacturing vice president, Bill Caulfield, and in getting used to Caulfield's brusque approach to people. This would take some doing, according to Regan, because Caulfield insisted on weekly conferences with all his division managers, and because Caulfield used this particular plant as a pilot plant—he usually checked on the manager every day. Caulfield was a highly respected man, Regan said, but tough-minded and very short on tact. "In fact," Regan added, "Caulfield frankly opposes the kind of human-relations management I want in this company."

Regan summed up Caulfield's viewpoint as "the old-fashioned bawl-'em-out school of thought." I thought I knew what Regan meant by this, but decided it might be better to explore Caulfield myself at first hand, with a minimum of preconceptions supplied by Regan. So I cut the meeting short at this point, and as I rather expected, this bothered Regan quite a little. I have found mighty few chief executives who don't expect to furnish, right off, all the information an executive recruiter could possibly need. Of course, I'll have to come back later, after I've located a good "fit-for-size" candidate on this Search #810, and have another go at Regan's opinions and attitudes.

**Friday, April 18**
Sometimes this recruiting work seems like a snap. Yesterday, as I was combing our bulging files on "available executives" for some man who might fit in over at American Toggle, Jim Rogers of Federated Brass phoned me for lunch, during which he asked if I recalled one of our high-school classmates named Harry Knowles. I remembered him only as a heavy-set football player, but Jim said Knowles had become a division manager in Federated's Tennessee subsidiary, and was one of the sharpest production men in the company. But just recently Jim had run into him in Nashville, and after three Gibsons, Knowles gave Jim a long story of woe, mostly to the effect that his boss never really let him alone and never gave him any real responsibility, etc., etc. Knowles had taken about all of this he could from the smooth-talking, paternalistic autocrat who is his boss.

I at once made a mental note that Knowles might be a possible candidate for our Search #810. I kept this idea to myself, of course, for I know that Jim is a loyal company man. Back at the office I put in a phone call to Knowles, said I was planning to arrive in Nashville Monday and wanted to ask his advice about a confidential personnel matter. Knowles of course seemed a bit surprised, and said he didn't think he could help me much but would be glad to see me Monday afternoon.

I continue to be mildly astonished at the readiness of executives to give advice to others on any and all subjects.

**Monday, April 21**

My conference today with Knowles went off about as I anticipated. He is still the big muscular chap he was in high school, and even if Jim hadn't forewarned me, I would have spotted his abnormally quiet way of speaking as typical of someone who is under pressure inside. First I asked him how things had been going for him, and he said O.K., that after twelve years with Federated Brass he felt he knew how to run a metalworking operation, "even though I didn't go to college." Then I outlined my job at American Toggle. After this presentation, I opened with the standard approach shot by asking him if, among the managers he knew, he might recommend one who could get along well with people, and also be willing to take on the challenge of helping to get American Toggle up out of fourth place in its industry—for $28,000 a year.

Knowles asked a few questions, mostly about how much room a new man would be given to operate under Caulfield, and how close were the relations between Regan and Caulfield. Though I could give him only superficial answers, these seemed to convey enough for Knowles. At any rate, he shook his head, and said he couldn't offhand think of any manager who would fit into the job at American Toggle. But after I picked up my briefcase to leave, Knowles cleared his throat and asked me if I could stay a few moments longer. I was then pretty sure he had taken the bait.

After we had both lit another cigarette and had chatted

briefly about his golf game, Knowles at last confided in me that he himself would be "very much interested in that job at American Toggle." I immediately expressed my pleased reaction and, to keep him on the hook while I explored his credentials, I assured him this was a totally unexpected piece of good luck. Said I would take the good word back to the company at once, and keep him informed of the situation. Knowles insisted on accompanying me to the elevator, and as we waited there, he let drop some valuable nuggets of information: said he thought all the talk about "getting along with people" was a half-truth, and that he would use tact and diplomacy whenever he thought this would serve the company, but he was not one of those "perpetual turn-the-other-cheek" fellows. I told him I was glad to hear this, because neither Regan nor Caulfield thought too much of meekness as an executive quality.

### Thursday, April 24

Got my first check on Knowles this morning from a pleasant young plant superintendent at Consolidated Tinplate in Hoboken. He had worked under Knowles during the war in a machine shop in Cincinnati. My main point in going over to see this Polish chap named Chelkowski was to start off by getting a view of Knowles as seen by a former subordinate, since I've found that the judgments of subordinates are consistently more revealing than those of superiors or peers when it comes to a man's ability to handle others. Chelkowski first told me that he considered Knowles a good shop foreman, because Knowles took the trouble to investigate every worker's complaint very thoroughly.

When I pressed Chelkowski to describe how Knowles got along with the men under him, Chelkowski would offer only rather mild criticisms. One point that did annoy Chelkowski was the habit Knowles had of repeating what others said before he answered them; he did this usually by introducing his remarks with a phrase like "I believe you mean to say . . ." Chelkowski admitted that this often did make his own statements clearer to himself, but he never got over being irritated by it.

Chelkowski remembered feeling really mad at Knowles only once. That was after Knowles was promoted to section manager and for some reason seemed to become antagonistic to the Polish workers; at any rate, Knowles once bawled several out for kidding each other and making jokes in Polish. Knowles told them they ought to speak English now that they were earning their living in America. But Chelkowski wound it all up by insisting that Knowles was respected, and "generally got along fine with employees."

This interview gave me some hints about Knowles that will certainly need checking.

### Monday, April 28

Today I found a banker in town who got to know Knowles rather well eight years ago when Knowles rented a summer cottage next to his on the Jersey shore. The banker was strongly impressed with Knowles's sociable manners, said Knowles had repeatedly shown "admirable self-restraint" both with his slightly quarrelsome wife, and also in disciplining his eleven-year-old son who was frequently in minor scrapes with other kids. After each episode Knowles never raised his voice at the boy, the banker said, but he would quietly point out to his son the unreasonableness or thoughtlessness of his behavior, and the boy always seemed to be very penitent.

How did Knowles get along with others at this resort? The banker's opinion was that Knowles's social personality and manners were excellent; he was "not too familiar" and "gained the respect of his neighbors." In fact, the banker thought Knowles himself might have made a most successful banker. This at least indicates that Knowles can adapt his social life easily in new surroundings. And his facility for staying calm with his son and his wife seems to indicate that Knowles doesn't simply repress his irritations at work and then release them on his family.

**Wednesday, April 30**

My lunch this noon with Mr. Horton, sales v.p. of Allied Closure, turned up some new pointers about candidate Knowles. Horton first knew Knowles when they were artillery lieutenants during the war, and he says Knowles then was a rather careless fellow who openly resented the Army's discipline and red tape. Knowles ridiculed the "spit and polish" regulations the commanding colonel insisted on. However, Horton was continually surprised at the way Knowles could quickly mask his feelings and put on a pleasant expression whenever the colonel showed up. Knowles seemed to be able to repress his emotional charge completely on short notice. These comments raised some further doubts about Knowles that will certainly need checking.

With enlisted men, Horton says Knowles was a marked favorite, partly of course because they heard him gripe so hard about regulations. Yet Horton noticed that none of the men attempted to become really familiar with Knowles; they would crack a joke with him now and then, but Knowles never seemed to let down the barriers to the point of personal exchanges about wives, families, civilian jobs, etc.

Shortly after the war ended, Horton says, Knowles called on him at Allied Closure as a job seeker. Horton, then a production supervisor, recommended him to the personnel department, which put him on the payroll under Horton as an assistant supervisor. In the first three months Knowles got such excellent cooperation from the foremen and workers

under him that productivity nearly doubled in his department. But then Horton was shifted to the sales division on a
management training program, and a cousin of the president
was appointed as Horton's successor.

This man, who came from another company, turned out to
be an irascible perfectionist who would bawl out foremen
and supervisors publicly, while generally ignoring the workers at the benches. Whenever Knowles attracted this manager's criticisms, Knowles merely put on that pleasant face he
had used with the colonel. But Horton soon heard that
Knowles and the new plant manager had had a ferocious
tangle over a sudden chewing out the manager had given to
one of Knowles's foremen.

According to the versions that reached Horton, Knowles
really let the manager have it, ridiculed his heavyhandedness
with people, and topped it all off by comparing him to a
stupid, flat-footed cop who kept his job only "by taking graft
from a politician." This really stung, not only because the
manager owed his job to the president, but also because he
wore big round-toed policeman-type shoes, and for the men
standing around at the time, the crack was a direct hit that
made them burst out laughing. This laughter goaded the
manager into a white-hot rage; he lost all control, called
Knowles a dirty name, and made a lunge for him. When
Knowles side-stepped, turned his back, and walked away,
the seething manager stomped back to his office, and ten
minutes later he called Knowles in and fired him.

Horton learned that the official reason for the firing was
"insubordination," and that's the way Knowles's record still
stands at Allied Closure. But Horton thinks this is very misleading, and that most of the blame belongs to that stupid
manager. However, I'm still suspicious of Knowles. It seems
pretty clear he not only doesn't like autocratic people, but
has repeatedly had trouble getting along with those directly

over him. Guess the time has come to take a close look at Caulfield, the man he would be working directly under at American Toggle.

## Tuesday, May 6

It's been a good while since I've talked confidentially to an executive as experienced, complicated, and mature as Caulfield. When I walked into his office yesterday afternoon he smiled quickly and waved me toward a chair beside his desk. Then Caulfield buzzed his secretary and told her he wanted no interruptions. When she mentioned a personal call he'd been expecting, Caulfield said he guessed that would have to wait, too, and his secretary's face reflected her private appreciation of his having made this decision instead of leaving it up to her. Then Caulfield turned to me, and without any prelude said, "I understand you want to find out just how tough I am to get along with." This was no man to dally with, obviously, so I immediately said I'd heard about his way with people and would like to hear what he thought about "human relations" in business.

He showed his intelligence right off by not dismissing the "human-relations" approach as so much nonsense. A great many companies, in his opinion, continue to be stupid about people; one wrong assumption they commonly make is that "people really don't want to work." Caulfield thinks this assumption is real nonsense; in his opinion "nearly everyone who isn't psychopathic likes to perform well," if he's got some standards to go by. That's why he thinks budgets, job descriptions, etc., are so useful. The trouble, according to Caulfield, is that sociologists and psychologists have sold a good many managements on half-truths, such as that if management wants improved productivity, it will have to let the workers participate in decisions, or develop what is now called "consultative leadership." In a lot of big companies,

Caulfield said, "it's now taboo for a manager to order people to do something; he has to learn how to persuade them to do it."

The results of such policies have been pretty terrible, Caulfield thinks. Among other things he pointed out that overemphasis on "human relations" makes people feel sorry for themselves; they tend to shirk responsibility, and to find excuses for their failures. He also thinks that managers who are trained to use "human-relations" techniques grow cynical, and come to believe that their job is primarily one of manipulating people according to some "management principle," or according to the smattering of knowledge they may have picked up as amateur psychologists. "Manipulating people is O.K.," Caulfield said, as long as a manager does so "fairly openly," and accepts "the realities of management."

When I asked Caulfield about these realities, he laughed, and said that every good manager has to use "timing" and "political strategy," and knows he may have to withhold some information for tactical reasons. Caulfield also holds that a good manager has to keep himself on guard against the pressures of group decisions, and must maintain a definite distance between himself and his subordinates.

But Caulfield immediately cautioned me not to pigeonhole him, and said he especially disliked the "glib formulas" he had heard from some managers. For example, the contention that the secret of good relations in industry is the application of the golden rule. Caulfield conceded that the golden rule is "a powerful corrective." But he thinks the management of a corporation and its people today is "just too damned complicated" to be solved by any one rule of behavior. Caulfield says, for instance, that he might bawl one man out for something that he'd never mention to another. It all depends on "who, when, where, and what."

With that, Caulfield ended the interview, and ever since then I've been wondering how a manager as expert as Caulfield would handle Knowles, and I'm convinced now it would be Regan who would trouble Knowles most.

**Friday, May 9**

Decided I'd better make a brief check on Regan's practices in managing others before I finalize my conclusions about Knowles as a candidate for Search #810. This afternoon I dropped in on American Toggle's industrial-relations director, Dick Ferguson, and soon discovered that Ferguson, an industrial psychologist, has introduced Regan to one human-relations technique after another. He says Regan now likes the idea of developing "group decision making" in the company. However, I learned that neither Regan himself nor his key men attend the weekly management-training sessions, because he feels "we are too old to learn these new tricks."

Ferguson doesn't seem to be fooling himself; he knows that Regan's lip service to the training program makes it superficial and probably a waste of time. But Ferguson is hoping he can carry his education of Regan in "human relations" far enough to get him interested in doing something about his own behavior, which Ferguson labeled as "defensive." By this he means Regan is "really autocratic," and regards human-relations techniques as a subtle means of controlling others. This, says Ferguson, is because Regan is "basically insecure" and "easily threatened by criticism."

When I asked Ferguson about Regan's tactics with subordinate managers, he said the boss was usually quick to reprimand almost any manager he happened to think wasn't doing his job, but was pretty careful not to annoy Caulfield or any of his men. Regan has a healthy respect for Caulfield's capacity for resisting interference from above.

Ferguson's information pretty well corroborates my own opinions about Regan. Now I'm ready to try out on Regan my proposition about Knowles.

**Tuesday, May 13**
When I went in to see Regan this morning, I handed him our complete résumé on Knowles, and while he was scanning this, I began commenting on Knowles's background and management record in detail. Regan had no questions until I referred to the way Knowles had resented any interference with his subordinates. It was obvious this really bothered Regan. He asked if Knowles knew that any good executive was often likely to check into things down the line, and skip the formalities of the chain of command. I assured him Knowles probably knew this all right, but that Knowles plainly believes that giving reprimands is the exclusive function of the immediate supervisor. Then I pointed out a most significant fact Regan had skipped over, i.e., that Knowles had blown his top only when a boss bawled out one of Knowles's subordinates.

Regan merely grunted, looked at me quizzically, and asked if I had learned about Caulfield's "bawl-'em-out system" of human relations. When I said yes, he said he therefore assumed I would not possibly recommend that his company install a touchy production manager under a tough executive like Caulfield.

This was about what I calculated Regan's view would be, and it gave me the opening to deliver a deliberately extended explanation of my separate estimates of Caulfield and Knowles. It was quite a speech, I guess, for I don't recall that Regan interrupted once. But the gist of my argument was fairly simple: I said that in my judgment being "good with people" is mostly a matter of character, and I tried to make it clear that by "character" I didn't simply mean traits like dependability and will power, but the whole bundle of constructive qualities that go to make up a mature man. Caulfield, I said, is the kind of executive who seems to have developed traits of character that earn the respect and confidence of subordinates, regardless of the fact that he bawls some of them out occasionally. These traits appeared to include sincerity, fairness, consideration for the growth of his subordinates, and a very sensitive appreciation of their individual temperaments. Caulfield also possesses many complex skills, such as articulateness, and the rare ability to motivate others by his own example. With all this equipment, I considered Caulfield fully capable of sizing Knowles up, and handling him successfully.

As for Knowles, I said I was sure he would never react to Caulfield as he had reacted to that colonel and the stupid manager at Allied Closure. Knowles apparently does have strong aggressive tendencies that have shown up in his sharp resistance to those encroaching on his authority. But I told Regan I was firmly convinced, after discussing this case with several psychologists, that if Caulfield ever did bawl out one of Knowles's subordinates, Knowles's respect for Caulfield would keep him from blowing his top.

At the same time I re-emphasized that Knowles's resentment of criticisms leveled at his subordinates indicates he has several very important qualities for getting along with people under him—e.g., consideration for the attitudes and feelings of subordinates, concern for their development, willingness to stand up for them, etc. These traits were apparently well appreciated by Knowles's men at Allied Closure, inasmuch as a group of them organized a farewell dinner for him.

I bet Regan that Caulfield would swiftly recognize and use Knowles's good traits and his desire for more responsibility. Caulfield, for instance, might keep expanding Knowles's responsibilities so that Knowles would have neither the time nor the inclination to develop any sizable charge of resentment.

When I was finally through talking, Regan shook his head, and I thought I saw my recommendation going down the drain. He said he didn't by any means agree with everything I'd said, especially my comments about Caulfield; he still considers Caulfield "too damn blunt with people." I was all ready for Regan's final rejection of Knowles, but he fooled me. Said he would take a chance on Knowles if Caulfield would. He got Caulfield on the intercom, and told him quite simply that a fellow named Knowles would be coming in to see him shortly about that production manager's job. Caulfield replied, "I hope he is tough," and as he clicked off, Regan grinned at me as if he knew Knowles would not last long under Caulfield. Personally, I'm glad Regan had the sense not to say anything more. It makes me feel American Toggle is going to be a more than reasonably cooperative client.

**Thursday, June 26**

Regan phoned me this morning that Caulfield has taken a big shine to Knowles in their first week of working together. But Regan said the two had already had a couple of warm arguments, and since they seem likely to have more, he asked me to come over and discuss the matter with him. When I arrived, Regan explained that while Caulfield seems entirely satisfied with Knowles, Regan himself didn't like his managers to be quarreling, and was suspicious of Caulfield's claim that Knowles is actually one of the easiest managers to get along with. Regan said the explanations Caulfield has given him sounded "like double talk"; Caulfield had assured him, for instance, that "Knowles can take frustration because he's getting aware of himself." Regan added that Caulfield seemed to think he'd given him the key to the whole situation by saying that Knowles "respects others because he respects himself."

I told Regan I was certain there was a lot more than "respect" involved in the good relations developing between Caulfield and Knowles. For one thing, there could be many complications of Knowles's attitude toward his subordinates versus his various attitudes toward authority; e.g., Knowles's concern for those under him, which seems to be a sign of real maturity, might enable him to do a good job even for a boss he did not respect. Nevertheless, I said that Caulfield's remarks did cover a good deal of ground; more ground, in this case, than might be covered by that hoary favorite, the golden rule.

Regan shot me a sharp look and asked what I had against the golden rule. Immediately I remembered that he is a conscientious churchgoer and president of the local Boy Scout executive board; so I merely said I thought it was very misleading to oversimplify this matter of getting along with people by wrapping it up in a single idea like the golden rule.

Regan accepted this generalization, but I suspect he will go right on giving lip service to ideas that he doesn't really understand mainly because he doesn't try to practice them. Top executives like Regan are still pretty common, but more and more executives today seem to be catching on to the complications of "human relations." I'm glad to say that one idea that seems to be falling into disrepute is the notion that the American corporation ought to become "one big happy family."

# CHAPTER EIGHT

*Dependability
and Conformity*

*The quality of dependability is generally—and erroneously—held to be one of the lesser attributes of an executive. Even those who possess it in large measure are likely to call it an undistinguished trait, common to those in menial positions. These opinions are probably the relic of old servant-master concepts; at any rate, many other traits that are repeatedly allied with dependability, e.g., reliability, punctuality, consistency, and thoroughness, reflect this same prosaic view of dependability. Actually, the expression of dependability in an executive is anything but prosaic. It is a quality that changes as a manager moves from echelon to echelon in a corporation, and it depends for its meanings on a complex of relationships between a manager's performance and the ethics and standards of the person making the judgment. These relationships are subtle and varied; yet at the same time dependability may be the most measurable of all the traits an executive may possess, being accumulated and registered day by day. It is measured not only objectively, by performance on the job, but also subjectively according to the evaluation placed on the "character" of the performer. Moreover, dependability is determined by the standards and the character of both the performer and the one sitting in judgment. Which is why a superior's limited views of dependability may block the progress of an ambitious young manager much less than the young manager's own views of this trait.*

*Finally, there is the danger of confusing the expression of dependability with the rigid or shrewd expression of conformity to a company's rules and procedures. Though these expressions may look alike, discriminating between them is essential for any who hope to understand the great trait of dependability.*

*In this chapter, some of the many characteristics of this trait are presented through the varying opinions of six different managers: a president, a division manager, two department heads, and two supervisors.*

TAYLOR D. HOPKINS, president of Tronic Instruments Corp., buzzed for his secretary and asked her to bring him the job-description file on the new customers' service department. Then he picked up his phone and called Division Manager Allen Teppard, and patiently waited while Teppard's secretary, who was always upset by these direct calls from "the chief," interrupted her own boss and finally got him on the wire.

"Al, just wanted to set the time for that first meeting on the new customers' service department." Hopkins spoke rapidly but without tension. "Could you and Fred Irvine and

Karl Bettinger come over this afternoon at three?" He did
not pause for an answer, for he knew Teppard liked to have
the whys and wherefores even when he expected to comply.
"We've got to find the right man to head up that new department, and I'm counting on you three to come up with some
good candidates."

"Sure, T.D., we'll be there at three," Teppard replied. "I
think Fred and Karl have already done some thinking about
this new job since you spoke about it at the last managers'
meeting." Teppard wished, for a brief instant, that Hopkins
could have given him a little more notice on this matter since
both of his department heads, Karl and Fred, were scheduled
to be tied up this afternoon. But Teppard did not think of
suggesting another time to Hopkins; he knew he was relied
on to comply with his boss's "suggestions," and Teppard himself felt wholly obliged to be on hand wherever and whenever Hopkins asked him to. It was part of what Teppard
meant by "showing character," and he derived a real sense
of pride in always carrying out promptly and exactly everything Hopkins asked. Teppard felt that pride now as he
heard Hopkins say, "Fine, Al, see you at three," and when he
heard the sharp click of the phone as Hopkins hung up, Teppard got that familiar sense of the confidence his boss had
in him. It reminded Teppard of his days in the army where,
as a young infantry officer, he had first keenly experienced
this sense of being depended upon by his superiors. Teppard
identified this sense with what he called "being a responsible
person"; those who did not feel depended on Teppard did
not consider reliable.

Teppard wondered what kind of manager Hopkins would
pick for the new customers' service department. He himself
thought that the most promising man was young Dick Todd,
one of Bettinger's supervisors who seemed able to get along
with Bettinger and his continual harping on "company

policy." Teppard at times still felt like chewing Bettinger out for always insisting on "going by the book," but he had long ago realized that Bettinger wasn't going to change his ways. Bettinger ought to be more like Department Head Fred Irvine, Teppard thought; Irvine was just as conscientious about following orders and policies, but he was quick to take any tip Teppard gave him, and he always let Teppard know what he planned to do, instead of going off stubbornly on his own, the way Bettinger so often did. Teppard realized that Irvine had his own faults; he was much too tense and inclined to be snappish with others; and he didn't seem to be able to handle Stanley Wainwright, who, in Teppard's opinion, was still acting like a spoiled child. Wainwright, a grandson of old man Wainwright who founded the company, apparently resented the fact that he wasn't being given preferential treatment; he undoubtedly would have got this if the Wainwrights hadn't sold out to the syndicate that put Hopkins in and reorganized the Wainwright company as Tronic Instruments Corp. Young Wainwright is bright all right, Teppard thought; but Teppard hadn't entirely approved when Irvine made him a supervisor a year ago, and now Teppard wondered why Irvine continued to put up with Wainwright's insolence. Maybe Irvine's afraid to admit he's wrong about the fellow, Teppard thought.

At five minutes of three that afternoon Department Heads Irvine and Bettinger were outside Teppard's office. Both men were quietly grousing about the inconvenience of interrupting their work when Teppard joined them. "Glad to see you could make it," he said quickly and as though he had given them a choice in the matter. Teppard believed in courtesies of expression, and in some measure his words now did soften the imperative character of his earlier message by phone ("T.D. wants to talk with us at 3 P.M. today about the new department head for customer service"). Teppard knew he could count on both men to come to his office first, as usual, and punctually at five minutes before the hour, in order to allow time to walk to the president's office together. During these little walks, Teppard usually briefed his assistants on last-minute points; but today he said nothing; he didn't want to let them have any hint as to the man he thought ought to get the new job.

When the three men reached Hopkins' office they were told by his secretary that he was busy on a long-distance call, and would be with them in a moment. They waited fully ten minutes, and Teppard found himself getting impatient; Irvine and Bettinger, however, seemed relaxed as they smoked and chatted together, and Teppard wondered why neither was annoyed (as he was) at the president's tardiness in meeting with them. Teppard felt that this delay by Hopkins—which was rare but not the first he had experienced—undermined the example of punctuality he had tried to set for his subordinates. But he quickly dismissed this thought as childish on his part; he knew Hopkins would have chided him for putting too much emphasis on being punctual, particularly when Teppard could assume that the phone call Hopkins was taking was important, else Hopkins wouldn't have taken it at this time. A moment later, when he saw Hopkins himself open his office door and call them in, Teppard felt he'd been a little disloyal to his boss.

"Sorry for the delay," Hopkins said. "A friend of mine over at G.E. I've been trying to get a hold of finally called me about their experience with their customers' service department, and I thought I could use a little more information on the subject before I talked with you fellows."

"Sure, T.D.," Teppard said, and Bettinger and Irvine nodded along with him.

"Well, you know what our problem is—finding the right man to head up our new department." Hopkins went right

to the point, as usual. "I've been thinking about that job, trying to imagine the kind of chap we want there, and I've
about concluded that the only thing he'd have to be is extremely dependable. We can set out his responsibilities easily
enough, give him the necessary authority and outline some
procedures. But we have to be sure he will deliver what's
required. If he doesn't, he could cost us a lot of good will, and
I've found that generally turns out to be very expensive."

"Could you give us an idea of what he'll be doing, mostly?"
Teppard asked.

"I'm not sure, Al, because that job description which was
drawn up by Organization Planning seems too all-inclusive.
This new department head ought to concentrate on keeping
our customers happy, and needn't bother about market surveys, scouting for new products, and the other things now included in that job description. His duties can be simple to
start with, like dealing with all customers' complaints and
following up on replacements. But he's got to be dependable
and trustworthy. I think you all know we don't want one of
those 'organization men' in this job; we don't want one of
those fellows who're afraid to stick their necks out a little,
and who insist on sticking to the rules no matter what the
circumstances. But we also don't want a fellow who's such a
nonconformist he won't follow the rules, and is afraid of what
a friend of mine recently described as 'sacrificing his individuality to the big bad corporation.' One little nonconforming
egotist like that could do a whale of a lot of harm in this
job."

Teppard waited until he was sure that Hopkins had finished, and then he said, "I think I know the kind of manager
you mean, T.D., and I'm sure Karl and Fred here do too. I'd
like to talk this over with them before we submit any candidates, if that's O.K. with you, T.D."

"Go right ahead, Al," Hopkins said, and then added,

"Could you let me have your choices before the end of the week?"

"Certainly," Teppard replied. He planned to have the final choice in Hopkins' hands well ahead of time, for he knew Hopkins was eager to get this new department going.

Teppard saw that the conference was over so far as Hopkins was concerned, and he turned at once toward Bettinger and Irvine. They caught the cue and started to leave with him. As they reached Hopkins' outer office, Teppard asked them both to be ready to discuss candidates that afternoon; he told Irvine to come and see him at four and Bettinger a half hour later. Teppard wanted to explore separately with each manager the capabilities of the men who might have what Hopkins was looking for; Irvine and Bettinger had each said they already had a good candidate for the job, but Teppard was determined to make sure both men understood what Hopkins wanted.

Department Head Fred Irvine appeared at Teppard's office right on the dot of four, and, as he anticipated, Teppard was ready and waiting for him. The only times Irvine could remember when Teppard kept him waiting were when Hopkins had unexpectedly interrupted Teppard's schedule, and this afternoon he knew Hopkins couldn't interrupt, since he had left for Cleveland. Irvine thought Teppard was inclined to be fussy about things whenever he had to wait for someone, and Irvine didn't want to upset his boss today, since he knew Teppard would probably be appraising him even while he himself was appraising his own candidate, Wainwright, for Teppard's benefit.

"Sit down, Fred," Teppard said, as Irvine entered his office. "We should be able to get through this job quickly. I think it will save time if I start off by giving you my opinion of Wainwright, the man you said you were proposing for this new department head. First off, I think Wainwright's a bit emotionally unstable; I've seen him blow off hard at men in his department on two different occasions, and maybe he was justified, but from what I saw he worked up too damn much friction. Then there's that habit he has of tossing out suggestions about things he doesn't know much about. You remember the time he told you the company ought to scrap its policy of supplying extra new parts with each installed machine. He just didn't know the score on that, and didn't know enough to keep quiet. But I guess my chief criticism of Wainwright is that he's not too reliable, judging from your reports on him in the past. For instance, I believe you told me he's inclined to give excuses whenever he hasn't finished a job on time, or exactly as you specified. To me, that's a sign he lacks character; he doesn't seem to realize his responsibility to carry out orders but instead seems to think his own ideas are better than anyone else's in the company."

Irvine appeared to take Teppard's criticisms of Wainwright without resentment, but when he replied his voice had a little edge to it. "I'll admit Wainwright's got some faults," Irvine said, "and he's irritated me many times, too. Still, I can't quite agree with you that he lacks character. I think he's very brilliant, and fellows like that are apt to be difficult to handle, now and then. Take for example that time you mention when Wainwright said the company's extra-parts policy was stupid; he did more than criticize—he recommended another policy that made a lot of sense, I thought. He suggested that the company, instead of supplying extra new parts, could adopt the policy of setting up a chain of grade A repair depots that would properly service all our machines, new and old."

"That's not a new idea," Teppard replied. "The Chief has been considering something along that line for a couple of years. Besides, we're not looking for originality in this new department head; we're looking for reliability and dependability, as Hopkins said."

Irvine didn't say anything for a moment, and when he spoke he seemed to be trying to please Teppard. "I see what you mean, Al, it's just that I think Wainwright has other qualities besides reliability. Guess what Wainwright needs most is more discipline to keep him in line with company policy. He's got to learn to obey better, and be more responsible about his job."

"That's right," Teppard said. "Obedience is the first lesson in learning dependability. It's not going to be easy, though. Wainwright is so damned proud of his grandpa, old man Wainwright, our founder, that he seems to assume only a Wainwright could run this company right. He's got to learn some humility—and that's lesson No. 2 in becoming a dependable manager. Take the Chief: he never boasts about anything, and he's always ready to admit his ignorance when he doesn't know much about something."

Irvine nodded. "I sure agree with you that training Wainwright to be like Mr. Hopkins is going to be a tough job, and I guess I've been too optimistic about his ability to handle that new customers' service department. I was counting on his brains to straighten him out once he got the job, but since Mr. Hopkins has said he wants a very dependable man in this spot, I'll withdraw Wainwright as my candidate. Right now, I'd have to rate him pretty low in reliability."

"Glad to hear you say so, because I've had my doubts about him for quite a while," Teppard said.

"Well, I'll keep bearing down on him," Irvine replied. "I've kept him following the exact orders on that Loeb deal." Irvine here saw a chance to remind Teppard of his own thoroughness. "I've been riding herd on that new policy of double inspections on rejected returns, Al, and it's tough going, but we'll make it stick."

"Good, Fred," Teppard said, forcing himself to sound approving. Actually, this particular policy was one he had strongly opposed in committee meetings with Hopkins and the other division managers. "I'll count on you to do what's necessary, in any case. Guess that's it for now."

As Irvine left Teppard's office he thought again how easy it was to please his boss if he just did things "his way," and was always careful to follow company policy. Irvine felt he had slipped in proposing Wainwright for the new job, but figured he had kept in Teppard's good graces by openly admitting his mistake. He would have preferred not to submit a candidate, and had done so only because he was sure Teppard expected him to. Irvine admitted to himself he would like that new department-head job for himself; at least it would be a change, and he was bored in his present position. But immediately the thought of taking on the new job made him worried, and he suddenly recalled Teppard's farewell remark about counting on him "to do what's necessary in any case." What did Teppard mean by this? How far would he expect a man to go in assuming responsibility? The possibility of having to act completely on his own made Irvine uneasy and tense; he tried to reassure himself by thinking that if he somehow did get the job, he could play it safe, as he did in his present job. Mostly this would mean checking with Teppard in advance on each new situation that came up, until he was sure he knew what Teppard expected of him and could act according to precedent. Still, Irvine couldn't shake the uneasy feeling that maybe Teppard expected him to take much more responsibility, and was waiting for him to show more initiative. Irvine wondered if he dared come right out and suggest to Teppard that he himself was a candidate for the new job; but he realized he did not have the nerve to do this, and as he returned to his own office and saw a lot of familiar papers strewn on his desk he told himself that this was after all a good job he now had. He was confident he could continue to convince Teppard he was doing the job Teppard wanted done.

As for Teppard, after Irvine left him he reflected that their decision to eliminate Wainwright as a candidate for the new job was perhaps reached a little too rapidly. Granting that Wainwright had all the weaknesses he and Irvine had discussed, it was nevertheless a fact that the young fellow was smart. Teppard admired brains, and he knew Hopkins was looking for "bright young men." Maybe, Teppard thought, we should have let Hopkins decide about Wainwright; after all, the Chief knew best what kind of man he wanted, and he might think Wainwright had more stuff than any of the others. But Teppard still thought Wainwright was undependable, and on that score alone he could be disqualified. In any case, Teppard would stick to the decision he and Irvine had made.

The thought of Irvine sharing in this decision disturbed Teppard momentarily. He realized that Irvine had merely accepted his boss's opinion, and had quickly given up supporting his subordinate, Wainwright. This was definitely a sign of lack of character on Irvine's part, in Teppard's opinion, and he resolved to speak to Irvine about it some time soon. Then Teppard realized that he himself liked the way Irvine usually did things; in fact he considered him a very steady performer. At least Irvine could always be depended on, Teppard thought, to keep his superiors posted on every action he intended to take; and Irvine never failed to follow policy. But Teppard wished Irvine would show more interest in doing things on his own.

The buzzer on Teppard's desk interrupted these reflections and he was reminded by his secretary that Department Head Karl Bettinger was waiting to see him. Teppard looked at his watch and noted that it was only four twenty; Bettinger must have seen Irvine leave his office; otherwise, Teppard figured, he would not have come a full ten minutes early. Teppard knew Bettinger was a bear for punctuality, and at the same time very critical of those who, as he put it, "fiddled around" waiting for others.

"Hi, Karl, glad you came right on up," Teppard said as soon as Bettinger appeared, and then immediately asked him, "Who's your candidate for the new department head?" Teppard had found that unless he forestalled Bettinger, the man was likely to launch out on a careful and useless explanation for anything he did that might be considered slightly irregular, even a little matter like being too much ahead of time for an appointment.

"My man is young Dick Todd." Bettinger sounded almost apologetic, as though he had been forced to say something he hadn't intended to.

"He is a real comer, all right, but I'd like to hear why you think he'll be able to handle this job."

"Well, he's a fine chap, really reliable." Bettinger looked sharply at Teppard. "I kept thinking of him when the Chief was talking about wanting a dependable man for this new customers' service department. Dick even looks dependable —he's a neat dresser, you know—and I can rely on him completely. He follows the rules and is always consistent."

"What do you mean, 'he's consistent'?" Teppard asked.

"I mean he's consistent in his thoughts and actions; they follow a good sound pattern. Dick's not taken in by all these newfangled ideas about 'delegation' and 'decentralizing authority'! He does his job the way I want it done, a real dependable supervisor." Bettinger sounded smugly satisfied, like one who had trained a pet to do his bidding.

"But what about that trouble in the tool room the other day?" Teppard asked. "I understand Todd assumed the authority to tell some of the men they could take tools home over weekends for their personal use. He didn't seem to be following the rules when he did this."

Bettinger frowned. "I chewed Dick out plenty for that stupid move," he said. "It won't happen again, I promise you. I was surprised at Dick; he just doesn't do things like that."

"He didn't hurt anything actually, Karl," Teppard said. "Maybe he should be credited with showing some initiative in a situation. The tool room men have been taking tools home for months, as it turns out, and Todd was sort of saving the company's face."

"Not as far as I'm concerned," Bettinger suddenly shot back. "We can't allow that kind of unpredictable action or everything around here will go haywire. Dick should have checked with me or you, first."

"Well, I'd be inclined to credit him with trying to do more than was expected of him," Teppard replied, almost casually.

"That could get him into a pile of trouble. I wouldn't encourage it." Bettinger sounded adamant. "I'm perfectly satisfied to depend on Dick to do his job for me. I don't claim to know all there is to know about managing, but I never found anything wrong with doing just what you're supposed to do. Dick's got brains, I know, but I don't propose to let him think he knows enough to throw the book away and do whatever he thinks best." Bettinger spoke so positively that Teppard realized once again how rigid a person he was, how resistant he was to changing anything, especially his own routines. Teppard didn't try to push him.

"I see what you mean," Teppard said. "Well, we both agree Dick is a good candidate for the customers' service department. You've always found him very dependable, and that's what Hopkins says this new job will require. I'll tell Hopkins Dick's one of the best possibilities we have to offer."

Bettinger nodded and grinned. "Personally, I think he's the best young manager in the company, Al."

"You're right, Fred, and that's just why I suggest you let him have his head just a little more, to see how he handles extra responsibility." Teppard saw Bettinger frown slightly at his suggestion. "I'll let you know," Teppard quickly added, "soon as Hopkins has reached a decision on this assignment. Better send me your file on Dick so I can fill the Chief in on any details he may want."

Bettinger nodded again, said "O.K. Al," and left. As he walked down the hall toward his office, he swore a little and told himself that Teppard was cockeyed about letting Todd have more leeway to act on his own. Todd just doesn't know enough, Bettinger reflected. But Bettinger knew he would have to give it a try because his boss had asked him to; if he didn't try, Bettinger knew he wouldn't feel right. He planned to let Todd have full responsibility for his department as soon as he could—that would be during the next half day that Bettinger had to take off for the overtime he normally put in on his own job. Teppard had started this overtime rule, Bettinger reflected, in order to prevent managers from overloading themselves, but even with Todd helping him now, Bettinger found he still had to work an extra four or five hours a week. It used to be eight or ten hours, and Bettinger wondered if he might not be able to give Todd still more to handle; but he concluded that Todd had all he could really take care of. Bettinger thought about how much he liked Todd and what a good supervisor the fellow was getting to be; he liked the way Todd always respected his superiors. Bettinger told himself he still trusted Todd completely, in spite of that incident about the tools which Teppard had brought up. He realized that if Hopkins picked Todd to run the customers' service department, that would leave him, Bettinger, with the tough job of finding some kind of substitute; and the prospect of this made Bettinger feel grim. It occurred to him he might hold on to Todd by giving him more responsibility than he could properly handle, and he tried to imagine what Teppard would say if he learned that Todd, acting on his own, had goofed up some important deal. But Bettinger knew he couldn't do this to Todd and face Teppard afterward; as soon as he got back to his office he picked up the phone and asked Todd to come in for a chat that afternoon.

Bettinger would have been shocked at what his boss, Teppard, was thinking about him and Todd. Teppard was trying hard to be patient with Bettinger's rigid ways, but he saw more clearly than ever now that the performance Bettinger expected of Todd was cramping Todd's experience as a manager. Teppard thought Bettinger must be almost totally blind to Todd's capabilities; like a school teacher, Bettinger seemed so strict about rules and procedures that he apparently never thought of giving Todd more responsibility. Teppard was glad Todd had pushed out on his own and broken the rule about letting the men take tools home for their personal use. Perhaps, Teppard thought, this meant that Todd was finally frustrated enough to risk showing initiative, even though he knew this would make Bettinger sore. But Teppard wondered whether Todd would really keep it up. He had noticed that Todd was always extremely meek and polite when he was with Bettinger. This was the way Teppard had seen many young men behave toward their superiors, and he found he often could not tell when this behavior was genuine or false. When it was genuine, the young man might actually be timid, or he might be simply respectful and ready to learn from someone smarter than he was. And when the behavior was false, the young man might be attempting to deceive his boss in order to avoid criticism, or he might shrewdly be conforming to what he thought the boss expected of him, in order to get ahead. Which was Todd's approach? Teppard suspected that Todd was being more than merely respectful toward Bettinger, but he was reluctant to accuse him of either deception or timidity as a manager. Teppard still expected Todd to become far more than the kind of highly dependable performer that had won Bettinger's full approval. If Hopkins chose Todd to head up the customers' service department, Teppard told himself, he would then as Todd's direct boss have a chance to see if he could depend on Todd to stick his neck out and take on more responsibility. Otherwise, Teppard realized he would just have to wait and see whether Todd would continue to let Bettinger confine him to routine management.

Shortly before five that afternoon Stanley Wainwright saw Dick Todd walking rapidly down the hallway outside Bettinger's office. "You look full of good news," Wainwright called to him, and Todd, who had been smiling to himself, stopped and smiled openly at Wainwright. "I guess I am, Stan," he said.

"What happened? Did Bettinger give you a gold star for perfect attendance?" Wainwright's scorn for Bettinger annoyed Todd, but he merely smirked at this old jibe. Bettinger's insistence on punctuality was a byword in the shop; the only time he was known to have been late was one icy morning when he fell and sprained his ankle on the way to work and, so the story went, a doctor forcibly delayed him until the ankle could be bandaged. Under Bettinger, Todd had made a point of being always on time, and it was now a habit he was conscious of only when someone made cracks about it. Sometimes he defended his habit as a useful time-saver, but with Wainwright he knew this would be a waste of breath; Wainwright was, in Todd's opinion, a fellow who seemed to enjoy making fun of others, particularly those who exhibited what Todd knew as "the old-fashioned virtues." Todd thought Wainwright was dumb to get that kind of

reputation for himself; but he knew Wainwright had a quick
mind and he usually enjoyed talking with him.

"What's new with you?" Todd asked.

"Come on, Dick," Wainwright replied, "don't give me that
innocent look. You must have heard the scuttlebutt about
that new department head they're going to appoint for the
customers' service department. The grapevine says you're
Hopkins' favorite for the job. Hasn't Bettinger tipped you
off yet?"

"You're kidding, Stan," Todd said. But he felt very good
about the rumor, and his thoughts raced back to what Bettinger had just been telling him, about his taking over Bettinger's department on Bettinger's next half day off. Todd
wondered if maybe this was to test him out before making
him the new department head. Might very well be, he
thought, but he wasn't going to let on to Wainwright, of
course. "I haven't heard any names mentioned in connection
with that new position," he said, "but frankly I'd like to get
a crack at some new job in this company. Meanwhile I'm
just trying to stay out of trouble and keep the paper work
moving."

Wainwright looked sharply at Todd and wondered if Todd
really didn't know he was the favorite to get the new job.
Todd appeared to be a confirmed "company man," a real
conformist, and Wainwright suspected he was pretending
now, putting on an act. "If you'd like that new customers'
service job," he asked, "why don't you drop the idea in the
Suggestion Box?"

Todd didn't think this was funny, and he replied somewhat
acidly, "If I had your name, I might try it."

Wainwright felt the sting of Todd's crack, and the sting
was sharpened by the fact that Wainwright could no longer
expect the benefits of nepotism. Wainwright now barely succeeded in controlling his anger; his tone of voice was strained

when he said, "The only thing that counts around here now is 'dependability,' according to what Irvine told me today. He said Hopkins is determined to get the most reliable man he can find to run the new department, and I didn't need a translator to tell me that Irvine was saying I'd never make the grade. He wouldn't think I was dependable no matter what I did, even if my name were Weintraub."

Todd laughed slightly. "Aw, I don't think Hopkins actually wants just an old plugger in that job. He's smarter than that. Sure he wants a dependable man, who wouldn't? But I think the guys who get a reputation for dependability generally wind up being considered what Teppard once called 'steady but unpromising.' That's for the birds. Trouble is, you've usually got to let the brass think you're one of these reliable joes, or they won't risk putting you up for promotion."

"Maybe you can fool a reliable old boss like Bettinger," Wainwright said, "but Irvine is a suspicious character, and not too dependable himself. I don't figure he could be fooled by a show of punctuality and exactness, simply because Irvine himself is trying so hard to convince Teppard that he's that kind of manager. Poor guy doesn't seem to realize that Teppard is asking for a lot more than that. I wish I were working under someone like Teppard who's got the guts to stick by his own decisions."

"Teppard's O.K.," Todd said. "I think he'd probably make a better president than Hopkins, actually. Hopkins strikes me sometimes as just a kind old gent who doesn't quite know the score. The other day he asked me how things were going and I told him, naturally, that everything was fine, and handed the credit to Bettinger who I said was a wonderful man to work for. You know, the old malarkey a boss always likes to hear. Anyway, it made Hopkins happy, and he obviously believed me. If I'd told him what I really think of Bettinger he'd have flipped. I'm pretty sure he could be fooled about a lot of other things, too."

"Maybe so," Wainwright replied, but he was sure Todd was wrong about Hopkins' being fooled. Wainwright was now bored with listening to Todd, and he changed his tone abruptly. "Lots of luck to you, anyway, on getting that department head job. Sorry I've got to run, Dick. See you around."

Todd watched Wainwright move off down the hall, and Wainwright's casual shuffling walk was faintly annoying to him. Wainwright ought to control himself more, Todd thought; he's just dumb not to try at least to look like a manager, and to act the way Irvine wants him to. Todd wondered why a man like Wainwright, with all his mental ability, didn't recognize the necessity of keeping his ideas and opinions more to himself. Being frank, Todd thought, was a good thing, of course; he recalled that one top executive he'd talked to in a management seminar had said that he always put a high value on an associate who would speak his mind openly—in fact, Todd recalled, that was what this executive had said he meant by a dependable manager. But Todd was sure this executive didn't mean the kind of bald frankness about people and things that Wainwright was capable of. Hopkins would agree with him, too, Todd told himself, and he suddenly felt good about all the pains he had taken to convince Bettinger he was the kind of supervisor who could be relied on to do things the way the company wanted them done.

Todd's views on Wainwright would not have surprised Wainwright in the least; indeed from time to time Wainwright made some of the same criticisms of himself. But he never could bring himself to accept Todd's angle on getting ahead. He thought Todd was dumb to "play it safe" with Bettinger all the time; Todd ought to remember, Wainwright thought, that his boss's boss, Teppard, was also watching Todd, and it might be much smarter to assume the traits of the highest-ranking boss one is likely to be noticed by, no matter how slight the notice. After all, Todd's boss could never be sure when *his* boss would recognize traits he liked in a subordinate manager, and since these traits would count the most in getting a promotion approved, Todd ought to be much more interested in copying Teppard than in copying Bettinger.

But these thoughts now gave Wainwright a sense of revulsion at Todd's calculating efforts to get ahead; and this reaction in turn stirred in Wainwright the feeling of responsibility he experienced when he thought of the small group of employees and foremen he had charge of and who were depending on him every day. Even his boss, Irvine, was depending on him, Wainwright thought, and he felt a twinge of pity for the man. Irvine, in his opinion, was a "nervous niggler" who was afraid to manage, and who, like Todd, kept trying to impress his superiors that he was "a company man." The phrase had once disgusted Wainwright, because it implied, among other things, that such a man was totally bound by bureaucratic rules. But now Wainwright was beginning to think differently about the idea; he realized the importance of feeling depended on by others in a company.

This was the kind of dependability, he reflected, that probably never occurred to a self-promoter like Todd; and Wainwright doubted if either Irvine or Bettinger had more than a dim sense of it. Teppard, he decided, must have it, or else he wouldn't have put up with Irvine for so long; but Wainwright thought Teppard should be doing a lot more to help Irvine manage on his own. As for Hopkins, Wainwright concluded that anyone in the position of company president who failed to sense that everybody else depended on him would be either a figurehead or a tyrant, and Wainwright was sure that Hopkins was neither. But Wainwright was not so sure that Hopkins was the kind of man who would be likely to see completely through the front that a fellow like Todd was putting on to impress his superiors. If Todd was the favorite for the new department head job, Wainwright mused, the reasons for this might be cockeyed but they would undoubtedly get Todd the job. Wainwright suddenly felt envious of Todd, and he wondered if he would eventually have to adopt Todd's tactics in order to get himself a promotion. The prospect repelled him, and he realized again how completely he was at the mercy of the characters and expectations of his superiors in the company. If he didn't conform to their ideas and standards of behavior, he told himself, they would think he was queer and unreliable. And if he did conform? He had always thought this meant he couldn't respect himself, and he still thought the way Todd conformed for his own advancement was debasing. The only excuse for conforming, he reflected, would be to benefit one's subordinates, to help improve the company; and in that case one's behavior wouldn't always be governed by company rules and the boss's expectations, since you would have to break the rules and oppose the boss whenever you thought this was in the best interests of your subordinates and the company.

The trouble was, Wainwright concluded to himself, it would be extremely difficult to know whether you were actually acting in the interest of subordinates and the company, or were rationalizing your behavior in your own interest, out of pride or anger. A self-serving man like Todd, he thought, apparently wasn't bothered by such inner difficulties; but Wainwright felt he himself could never be free of them, and that they would only grow more involved if he were given more responsibility. It was Todd, however, who was about to be given more responsibility, he reminded himself, and the frustration of his own situation irritated him intensely. He decided he would go to see Teppard as soon as the announcement about Todd's promotion came out. He respected Teppard and thought he might get some straight advice from him.

At eleven the next morning Teppard walked into Hopkins' office and told the president he was prepared to propose Dick Todd as the best candidate to run the new customers' service department. Hopkins looked surprised and pleased.

"I was pretty sure you'd be ready with your report before the end of the week," he said. "I hope you haven't felt rushed on this, but I'm damn glad to have your report. Dick Todd, you say? I sort of thought he'd be the choice. He's the fellow who assists Bettinger, isn't he?"

"That's right, T.D.," Teppard replied. "One of the best young managers we've got, in my opinion, the kind of reliable performer I think you're looking for for that position."

"If you say so, he must be, Al," Hopkins said. "I assume he's willing to take on more responsibility?"

"Well, I guess so, though Bettinger should have been giving him more chances to handle things on his own. I've asked Bettinger to give him the reins now and then. Todd's already shown some initiative in taking charge."

"Isn't he the chap who told the men in the tool room they could take their tools home over weekends?" Hopkins asked.

"Yes, T.D.," Teppard said. He wondered how Hopkins had learned about this, and guessed some talkative foreman had told him; Hopkins was continually picking up information from men down the line.

"I'm glad Todd isn't afraid to stick his neck out a little," Hopkins said. "I expect Karl makes him toe the line continually in that department. I've never heard of any other incidents about Todd before this tool affair, but I assume there must have been a few."

"As a matter of fact, that's the only time Todd has stepped out of line under Bettinger," Teppard said. "Personally, I wish he wasn't quite so meek with Bettinger, but Bettinger swears by him, and I must say Todd does an excellent job."

Hopkins looked thoughtful for a moment, and then asked, "Does Todd do more than Bettinger expects of him?"

"Not more, I guess," Teppard said. "But Bettinger says Todd always does everything that *is* expected of him, and that's kind of rare, T.D."

"You're right, it is rare, but not as rare as doing more than is expected," Hopkins said. "I was hoping Todd might have shown some signs of willingness to make the kind of extra effort you often make, for instance. However, you can't ask for everything from these youngsters." Hopkins paused and lit a cigarette before continuing. Teppard suspected he was not entirely satisfied with Todd, and wondered what else he might bring up about him. "Incidentally," Hopkins went on, "wasn't there anybody else who might possibly have qualified for this new post? Since the job won't be very difficult, I'd have thought there might be one or two others who could handle it."

Teppard was prepared for this question. "I think Todd's the only safe bet at the moment, T.D.," he replied. "The only other candidate I considered was Stanley Wainwright, who's been working under Fred Irvine as a supervisor. But Fred and I decided he just wasn't reliable enough."

"Wainwright?" Hopkins asked with some surprise. "That's right, he has been a supervisor for some time, hasn't he? But I thought Fred was having trouble pounding some respect into him?"

"That's one reason we didn't propose him," Teppard said. "And another is that he still comes in late a lot, and Fred complains that he wastes his time by asking too many questions about company policies and methods." Hopkins didn't say anything, so Teppard went on. "I'm convinced Wainwright isn't ready for any more responsibility yet. He's bright as hell, but hotheaded; and from what Fred says he can't be sure Wainwright will do exactly what he asks him to."

"Is he disobedient, or what?" Hopkins asked.

"Yes, he's disobedient, T.D.," Teppard said. "Wainwright's trouble is he hasn't learned the first two lessons in being dependable, that is, being obedient and being humble." Teppard liked this point about the two lessons that he'd made to Irvine yesterday. It summed up his own thinking rather neatly, he thought. But now he noted that Hopkins didn't seem to be paying much attention to him and appeared to be deep in his own ponderings. Teppard once again had the feeling he had probably been too hasty in eliminating Wainwright as a candidate for the new job, but he reassured himself that his reasons for doing this all made good common sense.

"I think your choice of Todd was absolutely right," Hopkins suddenly said. Teppard could feel himself relax, and he smiled involuntarily. "We've got to have a steady, reliable man like Todd in that new department," Hopkins continued. "Before we announce the promotion, Al, maybe you can help Karl a little in getting Todd to develop some more self-confidence. And keep him from sticking so closely to the rules and regulations. Let's plan to make the change-over in about five weeks; that should give us time to wind up the details, and Todd should be ready to shift for himself by then, too."

"O.K., T.D.," Teppard replied. "We'll get on it right away." He wanted to say something to show Hopkins he appreciated the way his decision about Todd had been backed up, even though he knew Hopkins didn't care much for such personal comments. But Teppard checked himself this time, for he sensed that Hopkins had some reservations about Todd that he hadn't expressed, and probably wouldn't express for some time, unless Todd actually flopped on the job, and Teppard was positive Todd wouldn't do that.

When Teppard had left, Hopkins spun his chair around and sat facing a window, his thoughts still on Wainwright and Todd. He told himself that Teppard had, without question, made the best decision in choosing Todd. Todd could be counted on to do a good job for the customers, all right; and he could be counted on to follow orders and procedures. But Hopkins now recalled the unfavorable impression he had formed about Todd after talking with him briefly a few times at the monthly managerial meetings. Todd, it seemed to Hopkins, was too busy being pleasant; he almost never offered an opinion of his own, but would very ably support those who were inclined to fall back on precedent and policy, those who suggested that a problem be handed over to the fellow who had been successful with similar problems in the past. And Hopkins remembered that Todd always seemed to be sitting or talking with some manager who was on a higher level than he was; one day Hopkins was watching Todd and some other young managers who were listening to Teppard tell a story before one of the meetings, and the way Todd strained to show his attentiveness, and then sustained his hearty laughter when Teppard had finished, appeared unpleasantly forced to Hopkins. At the time Hopkins thought, "He's on the make, all right," and he had wondered whether Teppard was aware of this. Was Teppard, Hopkins now asked himself, aware of it and still prepared to advance Todd as the best bet for the new department on the basis of his demonstrated reliability? His own question suggested to Hopkins that he might have overstressed the need for dependability in the new job; but he knew Teppard would not have proposed a candidate that didn't have other qualifications, too.

Nevertheless, Hopkins wasn't ready to abandon his conviction that Todd was a shrewd conformist, a man who was out to make himself appear to possess what he thought his superiors wanted in a manager. Hopkins now felt momentarily sorry that Todd was going to get his promotion, for he knew that unless Todd changed his attitude—and Hopkins didn't believe Todd would be likely to—he could not expect to go very much higher in the organization, at least not so long as Hopkins was around. But then Hopkins reflected that the promotion would get the new department started off on the right foot, since Todd obviously would be able to handle that job well; and the promotion could do Todd considerable good, too, Hopkins thought, if it reduced his unfortunate reluctance to assume responsibility.

Yet the irony of selecting Todd for this job struck Hopkins as he realized that he had warned Teppard and his department heads against choosing a man who had the kind of prosaic dependability that Todd seemed to have. Now that Hopkins thought of it, Stanley Wainwright was really much more the kind of man he'd been after. Of course, Wainwright's weaknesses, his temper and so forth, which Teppard had pointed out, made him a bad risk in this new job of customer service; still, Hopkins thought, Wainwright's willingness to question old policies, for example, seemed to imply the kind of intelligence and courage he was looking for. Whereas Hopkins was sure he would be able to predict practically every move that Todd would make in the new job, he wasn't at all sure about predicting all of Wainwright's actions. This uncertainty about Wainwright's behavior Hopkins found stimulating, and he felt a little regret that he hadn't taken a chance and arbitrarily selected Wainwright instead of Todd.

But almost immediately he laughed at the idea, realizing

that Wainwright's unpredictability was not really the kind
that could be depended on to be helpful to a company. Before a manager got *that* kind of helpful unpredictability,
Hopkins thought, he had to have a lot of other things: he had
to develop in himself traits like obedience and humility, as
Teppard had said, and he later would need to show per-
severance in overcoming obstacles, and courage in sticking
to his decisions, or perhaps in carrying out policies he didn't
agree with. He would also have to show he was ready to do
more than was expected of him, the way Teppard did. Eventually, Hopkins reflected, he would develop the kind of self-
confidence that long experience and know-how produce, the
confidence that allows a manager to side-step rules and
policies to get the best job done. By that time, of course, he
should be pretty high in the ranks, and loaded with responsibilities.

Then he would be a very poor executive if all his actions
were predictable, Hopkins thought; in fact, the more unpredictable his specific actions were, the better executive
he'd probably be. The one thing that would be predictable,
if he were that good, would be the success of his actions.
What Hopkins' own board was depending on him for, Hopkins thought, was continuously successful management, and
since this required continuous changes, he was generally
expected to deal with the unpredictable. One thing for sure,
the board didn't expect him to behave in ways that were
generally predictable by the competition. But their expectations went much further than this. He was being depended
on, Hopkins told himself, to demonstrate a capacity for the
kind of unpredictable behavior that would make the company continuously successful. This was not merely a large
order; it included, he thought, actually everything and
every quality that could be expected of any chief executive.

CHAPTER NINE                    *Fairness*

*The world of management seems to be amply supplied with men who, though sharply criticized by their colleagues on a variety of other scores, are still considered great executives because they are "always fair." This is a most powerful accolade: in effect it may fully pardon great weaknesses that the man may have exhibited in his executive life. Indeed, a reputation for fairness can offset practically any managerial shortcoming except that darkest of executive sins known as "a lack of integrity" (which is the concern of another chapter in this book).*

*The redeeming power of fairness in an executive, however, remains an exceedingly difficult quality to describe, for standards of fairness in management are by no means generally recognized. Some commonly approved practices—such as awarding executive bonuses strictly according to salary levels—are inevitably unfair. Conversely, an executive may be at his fairest precisely when he appears to others to be most unfair.*

*In this chapter the trait of fairness is explored in a fictional exchange of letters between a biog-*

*rapher and a publisher who has engaged him to
write the life story of the recently retired chairman
of a large corporation.*


Mr. Frank S. Pease
Chestnut Lane
E. Haddon, Conn.

Dear Mr. Pease:

Your manuscript on Mr. Charles L. Bartell, retired chairman of General Provision Corp., has been greatly enjoyed by those of the staff here who have had a chance to go through it. However, we are not all of the same opinion about certain passages, as I will presently make clear. Also, Mr. Bartell has now read the manuscript carefully and has returned it to us with his comments and rather sharp criticisms. I am enclosing his marked copy for your consideration.

Now I hasten to assure you that we are in no way disappointed in your work, Mr. Pease. It has all the sweep and historical authority we have come to expect from the foremost biographer of American business leaders, and we know we were absolutely correct in selecting you to do Mr. Bartell. Our selection also satisfied Mr. Bartell, who, you recall, characteristically insisted that if any biography was to be done of him, the task should be entrusted to a professional writer who would remain independent in his opinions and judgments of the subject, and who would be given a completely free hand in exploring the corporation's records and interviewing Mr. Bartell's friends and associates. Mr. Bartell confided in us that he was flattered that you had agreed to do this work.

Now, about the major objection that Mr. Bartell finds in
the present draft of the biography. He thinks you have, in
four different places, definitely undercut his reputation for
fairness by the manner in which you describe his dealings
with others. In addition, he says that you have reached conclusions about his character that are completely unwarranted.

Though we will not intrude our specific opinions on the
passages Mr. Bartell objects to, we do wish to raise a question that really bothers us in this connection. You have gone
to considerable pains to explain Mr. Bartell's reputation for
fairness as a square-dealing businessman, but the evidence
appears to be skimpy as to how Mr. Bartell acquired this
reputation. In fact, you mention only two incidents to explain it, and we frankly assume there must have been many
more early in his career. Perhaps if you included more of
these you might soothe the ruffled feelings of Mr. Bartell.

We will be looking forward to receiving your comments
on all this. Let me add that we are also looking forward with
pleasure and pride to publishing another masterful biography by Frank Pease.

> Cordially,
> ADRIAN THORNE

Mr. Adrian Thorne, President
Prestige Press Inc.
630 Fourth Avenue
New York, N.Y.

Dear Mr. Thorne:

Your communication on the Bartell manuscript is much
appreciated. I am a little surprised that Mr. Bartell has taken
exception only to my treatment of his fairness, and must

conclude that this fact is a good example of his tolerance, since in several chapters I felt obliged to take a rather critical tone about his lack of integrity at certain periods of his career. Yet I can understand how he might wish the ms. would more ardently support, rather than simply explain, his famous reputation for fairness. For in the year and a half I spent gathering research for his biography, I concluded that he is intrigued by the idea of becoming a legendary figure of American business, and it is extremely difficult for any human being to refrain from protecting a favorable though inaccurate image of himself that others may have acquired over the years. For this reason I think it would be useful if I first answer your main question about his early reputation for fairness before I answer Mr. Bartell's objections.

But before I reply to any of these queries, I propose to clear up a point that has obviously been responsible for considerable misunderstanding—i.e., the question as to what the word "fairness" means. I've spent a lot of time investigating the meaning of fairness as it might apply to an executive, and have found that executives themselves use nearly all the dictionary meanings plus a lot of other related meanings. The range in the dictionary gives you an idea of the remarkable elasticity of this word—*pleasing* and *reputable, freedom from blemish, injustice, and fraud, legitimate* and *equitable, honest, frank,* and *impartial, favorable, suitable,* and *distinct.* The executives I've discussed this word with seem to emphasize three aspects of fairness, which might be summarized as impartiality, consideration, and equitableness. However, every executive seems to have his own views as to how fairness is exhibited, and though a good many cite the golden rule, no two of them appear to have exactly the same standards of conduct in mind.

This is not so surprising, of course, in view of all that has been said and written over the last 2,500 years about the great basic virtue of justice, to which fairness is often related. After some study, I have concluded that fairness is always concerned with the distribution of things among others, and is essentially what Aristotle, Justinian, and others have referred to as "giving every man his due." Since this distribution, as Aristotle points out, "must be according to merit in some sense," it is no wonder that men disagree so frequently as to what is fair. Each has his own ideas as to the merit of others, and hence as to what others deserve, in fairness.

With this somewhat philosophical introduction, I will proceed to the point you raised about the apparent scantiness of the evidence as to how Mr. Bartell acquired his reputation for fairness. Your remarks make me realize I have not in the ms. sufficiently underscored the fact that Mr. Bartell's widespread reputation for fairness actually stems from the two incidents I described.

As I have related in the ms., Mr. Bartell first earned his reputation during the Twenties, when he was one of the very few executives who held that workers under a piece-rate incentive system were entitled to all the extra pay they could earn. This was pretty heretical then, for the common management practice was to reduce the piece rates as the productivity of the workers went up; and this tightening of rates was—and in a few plants still is—considered smart management. But Mr. Bartell attacked it as "an act of gross injustice." When his criticism was not echoed by other executives, it was largely ignored by the press, but almost immediately some union leaders rushed to his support by calling him "the square dealer," and the name caught on with the rank and file. After that, a good many newspaper editorials commented sarcastically on Mr. Bartell's nickname, suggesting he was all for giving his company away to the workers.

The company, however, continued to flourish and expand,

and a couple of years later one of the presidential candidates who was seeking the labor vote began praising Mr. Bartell as "the square dealer" in his campaign speeches.

That about made his reputation for fairness, nationally. But the most dramatic and probably the best-known story about his fairness is the one about how he applied the golden rule back in 1932 when he dealt with that gangster who was determined to muscle in on the company's trucking business. Mr. Bartell is one of those numerous businessmen who hold that the golden rule is a sure guide in handling people, especially in treating them fairly. The idea that you should treat others as you would want to be treated seems quite generally accepted as a way to ensure fair treatment. Practically, though, the rule can't be indiscriminately applied; as I have pointed out in the ms., most other executives would have been extremely cautious with this crook and many would probably have tried to outsmart him through some legal maneuver. But Mr. Bartell, so the story goes, followed his own advice about using the golden rule, and treated this ex-convict as though he were a completely honorable gentleman, even to the extent of trusting him with confidential information on the company's trucking profits. As a result, the gangster is said to have responded as Mr. Bartell had expected him to—i.e., the man treated the confidence just as honorably as though he were an entirely trustworthy person and, what is more, dropped his demand for a cut of the company's trucking revenues.

I don't know how often this story has been repeated, but I do know that most of the people I discussed it with accepted it as proof positive that Mr. Bartell is a paragon of fairness in the business world. Actually, this story doesn't illustrate fairness, and reduces the character of Mr. Bartell nearly to the level of a pious and not-too-bright do-gooder, which he is not and never was. For this reason I have attempted to debunk this tale by adding Mr. Bartell's full explanation: that he never showed the gangster anything more confidential than the costs of running one truck and a table of published figures on the company's past profits. Mr. Bartell also concedes that the gangster may have been persuaded as much by what to him looked like slim profits as he was by Mr. Bartell's treating him like a man of honor. But the old story is a legend now, and though I have added this explanation, I have no faith that it will have any appreciable effect. Few things seem to die so hard as sentimental stories about "hardheaded businessmen."

The point I wish to make, in any case, is that Mr. Bartell's widespread reputation for fairness rests predominantly on a couple of well-publicized incidents, one of which is a compound of distorted facts. In addition, Mr. Bartell gives the personal impression of one who would act fairly; the first time I talked with him at his estate at Locust Valley his erect carriage, calm visage, and courtly manners all conveyed the strong impression of a man of fine character. But to get a clear view of his fairness you have to dig into the personnel history of General Provision Corp., and then check your findings with Mr. Bartell and again with his associates in the company. When I did this, I rather quickly found the usual curious agreements and contradicitions.

I was not too surprised to learn in early interviews with Mr. Bartell's associates that while they disagreed about some of his other traits, they were unanimous in saying "he's always fair." Such unanimity in the preliminary phases of the interviewing is a familiar story to me after years of writing the biographies of businessmen, and I know it will nearly always disappear when I begin eliciting confidential memories and opinions. I confess this continues to intrigue me, and perhaps the chief reason I undertook this study of Mr. Bartell was because I wanted to describe how it is that the associates of a successful businessman can readily credit him with a quality like fairness, even when they all privately hold such different ideas about the quality, and about the boss's real claim to it.

Now I will take up each of the passages in the manuscript that Mr. Bartell objects to, and will try to make entirely clear why I wrote what I did. I am quite sure that my analysis of the episodes described in these passages will at least demonstrate how difficult it is for one human being accurately to credit another with the virtue of fairness.

*1. The Very Helpful Letter*—The passage Mr. Bartell has marked on page 23 of the manuscript describes how, in May, 1928, when he was president of General Provision Corp., he received a letter from one of his old Cornell classmates, who asked his help in getting a job with General Provision's plant in Easton, Pennsylvania. The classmate explained that he had recently lost his job as plant manager of a competing food company, and said he now wanted to work for General Provision Corp. because he had always greatly admired "Brother" Bartell and his business policies. Obviously trading on sentiment, the man reminded Mr. Bartell of their mutual fraternity associations and college escapades.

Mr. Bartell promptly replied to this appeal by saying he was not going to help his old friend get a job, but instead gave him some familiar advice to the effect that the man should rely on his own efforts, that favoritism was not to be trusted, and that even Mr. Bartell's own son would be getting no help from his father. Mr. Bartell concluded his letter by suggesting that, if the man really wanted to work for General Provision Corp., he might try "storming the gates" of one of the company's plants until they gave him a job.

In the manuscript I have followed this story with the fact— discovered from an old letter in Mr. Bartell's personal files— that Mr. Bartell, on the same day, had written to the Easton plant manager asking him to keep his eye out for a Cornell man named such-and-such who might be coming to see him, and Mr. Bartell asked the manager to "see what he could do and perhaps give him a chance to do it."

I scarcely needed to tell the reader that such a letter from General Provision's president was tantamount to an order to hire the man, and that after the man got the job he would in all probability be known on the company grapevine as "that friend of Mr. Bartell's." Mr. Bartell objects that these conclusions are unwarranted. I can only say, in reply, that they are completely supported by all those in and out of the company with whom I have discussed this incident.

Mr. Bartell further objects that this incident reflects seriously on his sense of fairness by implying he showed favoritism and gave dishonest advice. I do not disagree with these implications. The chief point of the story is that Mr. Bartell made no effort to check the man's competence before helping to open up a job for him. He conceded this when he told me the story, saying he had assumed that, as an ex-plant manager of a major competitor, the man would have enough experience to qualify him for some job with General Provision, and he expected the Easton plant manager would check on the man's ability. In short, Mr. Bartell, in my opinion, acted unfairly in two ways: (1) he facilitated the award of a job to a man without regard to his merit; (2) he took away a job opportunity that others might have deserved.

Mr. Bartell argues that his two letters in this case were "sincere efforts to be fair." The first letter, he points out, did not promise the man any help, but urged him to use his own initiative; and the second letter did not order a job made for the man, but asked the plant manager to use his own judgment. I recognize Mr. Bartell's sincerity in this matter; but I maintain that his sincerity of purpose did not affect in any way the fact that what he did was unfair.

2. *The Hard Bargain*—The passage objected to on pages
56 to 58 concerns my brief presentation of the deal Mr. Bartell offered his first business partner, Philip Porter, back in
1909. The description of the unusual terms of this deal is
contained in two paragraphs, as follows:

"After five years of working to build up a drygoods business with Porter, Mr. Bartell concluded that they would have
to part company, chiefly because Porter was such an egotistical and dictatorial manager. Porter constantly irritated both
customers and the firm's employees, and on many occasions
customers had canceled big orders and good salesmen had
quit. Mr. Bartell spent considerable time pondering how he
might get Porter to withdraw, and finally one day he forth-
rightly told Porter that he wanted to dissolve the partnership.
Then he presented Porter with this proposition: either partner could buy out the other, or sell out to the other, for 40
per cent of the firm's net worth. The business by then was
worth some $50,000, or five times what the two men had
originally put in. Mr. Bartell gave Porter first choice as to
whether he would buy or sell.

"Porter at once accepted this method of settling matters,
but he asked, as Mr. Bartell felt sure he would, for twenty-
four hours in which to decide on his course of action. In this
period Porter found out what Mr. Bartell already knew—i.e.,
that the best men working for the firm would not remain if
Mr. Bartell withdrew. The next day Porter wanted to back
out and argued that in view of the firm's potential earnings
he deserved, as a selling partner, to get at least 50 per cent
of the firm's current worth. But Mr. Bartell held him strictly
to his agreement to the terms of the proposition, and bought
him out for the bargain sum they had agreed on."

I realized some time ago that I should have expanded my
analysis of this deal in the ms. to show exactly how it illus-
trates Mr. Bartell's fairness, and I am including in this letter

the following paragraphs, which I have drafted to clarify this matter:

"Many people are likely to agree with Porter's daughter-in-law, who bitterly contended that Mr. Bartell "tricked" her father-in-law into selling out. Such a judgment would be very unfair to the remarkable sense of fairness Mr. Bartell himself exhibited in this deal. First, consider some facts about Porter as a partner: his faults as a manager were plainly exhibited in his irritation of customers and employees; such behavior, which lost the firm orders, was clearly unfair to his partner. He was in fact so poor a manager that he was completely unaware of the low opinion which others in the firm had of his managerial ability. Thus Porter had forfeited the right to share equally in the growing business of the firm.

"Now consider Mr. Bartell's behavior as a partner. He was credited by contemporary businessmen as well as by the firm's employees with the success of the firm. He carefully thought through the offer he made to Porter; although he knew that Porter hadn't contributed much to the partnership beyond his original $5,000 investment, Mr. Bartell was willing to allow him, in effect, a 40 per cent share in the firm. Mr. Bartell's proposition offered each partner the same financial bargain, and he gave Porter first choice at this bargain.

"Now consider the two points about the deal that Porter's daughter-in-law considered tricky on Mr. Bartell's part: (1) the fact that Mr. Bartell did not tell his partner the firm's best employees would not stay on if Porter bought the firm; (2) the fact that the price Mr. Bartell named in the deal looked like a bargain for Porter if he bought, but actually became a bargain for Mr. Bartell when Porter realized the situation and sold out to him.

"The answer to the first point is that Mr. Bartell, having told Porter that the partnership would have to be dissolved, was offering him a straight business deal, and both men were thereafter free to use the most effective tactics they knew. Porter could have flatly refused the deal and countered with one of his own. But once he accepted Mr. Bartell's proposition, he assumed whatever risks it contained. He obviously accepted it as a business deal, and by his speed in doing so he plainly showed that he hoped to get a bargain at Mr. Bartell's expense.

"The answer to the second point of criticism about the deal is that it assumes that a partner in a two-man firm is always entitled to a half share of the business. In deciding that Porter deserved less than a half share, Mr. Bartell relied on his own judgment of the man's equitable share in the firm, and then showed his fairness by allowing Porter a greater share of the firm's value than Mr. Bartell thought he really deserved.

"It can be argued, of course, that Mr. Bartell could have negotiated a sellout price with his partner. However, Mr. Bartell knew that Porter was egotistical and greedy, and that as seller he would undoubtedly demand a full half interest. Since this was, in Mr. Bartell's judgment, far more than Porter deserved, Mr. Bartell would have been guilty of agreeing to a division that was grossly unfair. To protect the firm and its employees, Mr. Bartell had to remove Porter as a co-manager, and he did so by a deal that was eminently fair to Porter."

I shall be interested to hear what Mr. Bartell thinks of this appraisal. He could, in my opinion, consider this deal one of the clearest proofs of his quality of fairness.

3. *The Heir Apparent*—In the incident described on page 178 of the ms., Mr. Bartell's sudden decision, in 1952, to sidetrack the man he had been grooming as heir apparent for ten years undoubtedly conveys a rather unpleasant impression of Mr. Bartell, but I ask you to note that I have neither expressed nor implied any reflection on his fairness in the pas-

sage where I take up the shifting of his attentions to a new heir apparent. This decision was, in fact, the only thing he could rightly do, once he became convinced that his long-time favorite, a prodigious salesman, was just not capable of directing the production side of the business. Furthermore, this favorite was so assured of his future that he had become increasingly offensive to several key executives who dared to criticize his decisions.

However, Mr. Bartell did fail to treat his former favorite fairly. In abruptly shifting the man from the executive vice presidency to a staff vice presidency of marketing, he made no explanation of this matter to other executives in the firm, and gave the ex-favorite no chance to save face. In fairness to the man, Mr. Bartell could, for example, have given him a chance to resign first. Mr. Bartell told me that he might have done this had he not been so bitterly disappointed in the man; he was so intensely irritated by the man's arrogance that he lost his usual objectivity and decided to reprimand him severely.

*4. Self-Dealing*—Mr. Bartell takes strong exception to what I have said on page 148 about the large bonuses that have been so steadily awarded to the officers of General Provision Corp. In reply, I point out that my comments are based almost entirely on an extensive study of the company's compensation policies and a survey of the last twenty years' bonuses, which the treasurer of the company supplied to me. In that period I found no evidence that the bonuses bore any rational relation to the fluctuations in sales and profits. The bonuses went up or stayed the same, but never dropped, even in the four years that General Provision lost money.

Now I had fully expected that Mr. Bartell's sense of fairness would have kept him from approving bonuses in un-profitable years. However, he does not even seem to have been conscious of any unfairness in awarding annual bonuses that were rigidly related to salaries instead of approximately related to each individual executive's contribution to the operations of the company year by year.

In discussing this matter with me, Mr. Bartell said he had long since chosen to make each executive's bonus a fixed percentage of salary because he believed that salaries were roughly according to merit, and he didn't feel capable of judging the individual performances of his executives and rewarding them accordingly. In talking with me, however, he conceded that some of his executives often hadn't really earned the bonuses awarded to them.

In view of Mr. Bartell's admissions concerning his handling of the bonus awards, I am obliged to say in the ms. that he appears in this instance to have been wasting the moneys of the corporation. By dispersing extra rewards that had not been earned by extra executive efforts and positive results, Mr. Bartell was treating his executives unfairly. He did not, that is, attempt to give to each man—including himself—his due. The extreme difficulty of doing this is one reason, of course, why over half of all corporations in the country do not pay executive bonuses.

To expunge any of the foregoing incidents from the biography would, I believe, remove evidence needed to place Mr. Bartell's reputation for fairness in proper perspective. As it is, I am not entirely satisfied that these episodes really offset those striking cases of fair dealing that make Mr. Bartell so legendary an exemplar of this quality. All these other episodes, of course, I have included in this manuscript, and I have done my best to verify the facts that support them.

For example, the presidents of two of Mr. Bartell's toughest competitors double-checked the story of how Mr. Bartell's extraordinary talent for managing people had time and again in 1944 prevented the collapse of meetings on War Production Board problems. They are convinced that his skill as an intermediator in situations involving conflicting opinions is based chiefly on his extremely high sensitivity to the presence of mounting emotional pressures in other people. As a chairman, he would sense a potential explosion, and neutralize it, long before any but the antagonists at the meeting thought anything was brewing.

Far more remarkable evidence of his fairness, I think, is his ability to recognize his own prejudices against others and to keep these under control. As he has told me, whenever he feels irritation rising in him against another man in a conference, he will rigidly confine himself to getting more facts by asking questions of the man, and if this does not make his own feelings subside, he will arbitrarily adjourn the meeting and give himself a day or two to recover his detachment before calling another meeting. His ability to do this marks him, in my judgment, as one of the rarest and fairest executives I've ever heard of, and I have clearly said so in this manuscript.

Yet I suppose that to outsiders Mr. Bartell's fairness was most convincingly demonstrated five years ago when a fire destroyed most of the company's main plant. The disaster struck just at a time when three of General Provision's major suppliers were about to make their major annual shipments to the company. Technically, according to the purchasing contracts, the fire relieved General Provision of responsibility for accepting the shipments. But, as Mr. Bartell knew, the sales managers of these suppliers were heavily dependent on General Provision's orders, each had spent considerable sums that year to meet emergency shipping schedules, and if they couldn't ship the goods they would have to spend still more money storing them until General Provision could rebuild. In Mr. Bartell's opinion, these sales managers deserved to be treated fairly, regardless of what the fine print in the purchasing contracts said about disasters; and regardless of the cost to General Provision. So Mr. Bartell called his purchasing manager in and directed him to get off a wire immediately, telling these sales managers that General Provision would accept and pay for all shipments, as scheduled. Then he told his plant manager to start looking for suitable storage space nearby.

To General Provision's own executives, I think Mr. Bartell proved his fairness most exceptionally in the salary deal described on page 221 of the ms. Shortly after the war, inflation began to squeeze the salaries on middle and lower management levels, but Mr. Bartell, like many chief executives who had held their jobs for years, continued to think his own salary as president, $85,000 a year, was ample; and he also thought he was saving the company money by refusing to let the directors increase it. For some time he seems to have overlooked the fact that none of his subordinates enjoyed the very sizable income (up to $75,000 in some years) he received in the dividends and capital gains afforded by his extensive holdings of General Provision stock. But one day his second-in-command told him he was resigning to accept a higher-paying job, explaining that there seemed to be no chance of breaking through the salary ceiling that Mr. Bartell's salary automatically set. (Typically, the ceiling of this top vice president was about 70 per cent of Mr. Bartell's salary, while the No. 2 v.p. got about 55 per cent, and all middle management salaries were well below 35 per cent.)

Once Mr. Bartell realized what his fixed salary was doing, he ordered a study of General Provision's compensation levels, and shortly thereafter recommended that the directors double his salary, in order to relieve the squeeze on salaries all down the management line. However, what made Mr. Bartell's move fair was his insistence that, before any salaries were changed, all managers' jobs be analyzed and corresponding salary ranges developed for each job. This uncovered many inequities in pay rates, which were gradually removed by promotions, early retirements, and transfers of personnel. Thus Mr. Bartell did his best to be fair to his subordinates according to their individual merit.

Now, in conclusion, I wish to answer Mr. Bartell's general comment that I have omitted all references to his fairness in situations involving the SEC and stockholders. He cites the case where the SEC in 1949 charged the company with making "unfair representations" in a new stock offering of General Provision common; and he points out how he was able to show conclusively that the offering was "absolutely fair and square."

I realize that Mr. Bartell sincerely believes this is an example of fairness, and there are many people who would agree with him. However, I stand by that definition of fairness which I explained earlier—i.e., that this quality is demonstrated in the division of things according to the merit of individuals. Therefore, I hold that fairness is not involved in dealings with inanimate objects like corporations, or with undifferentiated groups, such as stockholders. There is no such thing, in my judgment, as a "fair" division of a corporation's profits among employees, stockholders, and the corporation; or a "fair" price for the customers.

Such groups cannot "deserve" a certain portion of something; there just aren't any generally recognized standards of merit to go by. Among such groups, the division of rewards is based partly on their relative political and economic power, partly on market supply and demand, partly on legal rights, and partly on custom. A corporation that gives its stockholders only a 1 per cent return, and its employees a profit-sharing award amounting to 40 per cent of net income, is, as I see it, being neither fair nor unfair to any of the groups involved, for there is no measure of what is due to each. Custom and practice have set up rough guides such as a 5 per cent dividend, a 20 per cent return on investment, a 40 per cent markup, etc., but there is nothing essentially "fair" about such figures, in my estimation.

Mr. Bartell, of course, may dispute these ideas about fairness, but I will have to revise my present estimate of him if he will not agree with what another experienced chief executive told me a while ago: "A man can have the reputation of being fair, but I doubt that any executive can always be fair."

Cordially,
FRANK S. PEASE

CHAPTER TEN        *Leadership*

*The achievement of leadership in industry is the rarest and most difficult of all managerial achievements. Yet executives as well as laymen continue to assume that an industrial leader is a fairly common phenomenon. And the social scientists, for their part, have generally reduced corporate leadership to the level of behavior exhibited by an expert conciliator and coordinator. Real industrial leadership is far beyond these techniques of administration; it is also far beyond the powers of invention, or personal aggrandizement. What leadership is, however, continues to defy exact description.*

*In this chapter, management consultant Phil Cadmus expresses his convictions about leadership in a letter to a friend in one of his client firms who has been appointed by a prominent trade association to help nominate "the year's outstanding business leader." The nominee is to be cited for his specific "qualities of leadership" and Cadmus' friend has become confused by the plethora of statements that prominent executives have made about leadership in American industry.*

My dear friend:

I am not surprised that you feel dumfounded by the diversity of opinions your contemporaries in management have put on the record as representing their understanding of leadership. You've accepted a tough and thankless job, and I cannot promise that you will by any means see eye to eye with me on this subject. However, I will certainly attempt to clarify industrial leadership for you.

So let's begin, and probably the simplest starting place is with those statements about leadership you've run across. Your samples are relatively modest; I assure you that you could multiply them many times, if you really tried. But two or three of yours will make the necessary points.

Let's take that statement made by General Electric's Chairman Ralph Cordiner: "The hallmark of leadership is the ability to anticipate the reasonably foreseeable needs of tomorrow and beyond tomorrow with at least some clarity and confidence." By itself, this statement by the head of a great manufacturing corporation might readily be taken to mean that leadership is essentially a matter of economic foresight. However, as you would discover by reading further in Cordiner's book, *New Frontiers for Professional Managers,* he includes in his summary of future challenges and opportunities not only the areas of long-range planning and communications for decision-making, but also "the baffling area of human motivations," which would involve managers with such questions as "what do people want out of life and how can these human aspirations be realized in their daily world." This is an extremely large order, you will admit, but Cordiner courageously believes that ways and means will be found to answer these challenges.

In fact, Mr. Cordiner in his book says one of his deepest desires is to "help every man and woman in the organization find a sense of true participation in working toward high and noble objectives that will bring everyone a sense of pride and satisfaction." What is more, he believes this goal of his is relatively common: "The great dream of the professional manager is that someday he will find a way to share with his associates a mutually deep vision of what a truly inspired organization can achieve." It is difficult to imagine a more ambitious goal for industrial leadership. The point here, however, is that Mr. Cordiner speaks of leadership specifically in terms of two qualities (foresight and confidence) aimed at a goal of human experience that assumes tremendous changes in the nature and attitudes of managers and workers alike.

Now when you turn to the words of Mr. Crawford Greenewalt, du Pont's president, you get a different picture. The dull-sounding quote you found is accurate enough, but it too is taken out of context. He did say, "I have no doubt that leadership is, in fact, an important executive attribute." But in his book, *The Uncommon Man,* he goes on to say that "I am not at all sure that it [leadership] is more than a small fraction of the answer," and he cites a clergyman and a soldier as examples of men exercising leadership through "ethical thought," courage, and personal example, but who do so without the need of executive talent. He adds, "I have known men with leadership, with judgment, with vision, who were not in any sense of the word good executives." This is a discerning comment, for it clearly marks a distinction between executive ability and leadership, and this distinction, I need not tell you, is one that is scarcely ever made. In fact, the common tendency is to assume that the head of a big corporation is, ipso facto, a leading executive, even though his claim to notice may be only an exceptional shrewdness— or something he'd rather not talk about. How many times have you sat and listened to speeches that hailed some chief executive of a corporation as "a great leader of American business," when you, and many others present, knew that the fellow got and held his job primarily through family or political influence, and, on his own, probably couldn't manage anything much more complex than a lemonade stand?

Though you know that the term "leader" has been pathetically overworked by businessmen, you may not know that in the last few years this term has also been overworked —or perhaps I should say worked over—by a lot of psychologists, sociologists, and other social scientists. Maybe you think this isn't anything to be concerned about, but in my observation the ideas about leadership that these fellows have been spreading within management have already had some pretty unfortunate effects. For instance, there's the idea that leadership is primarily a matter of group behavior, i.e., it is the performance of acts that "help the group to achieve its objective." These acts would include helping to set the group's goals, moving the group toward them, improving the interactions among the members, their cohesiveness, and various other things with odd-sounding names like hedonic tone, syntality, and permeability. You can see that this not only plays down the individual qualities of a leader, but assumes such dubious things as that a group of people can and should decide what the group's best objectives are. In short, the democratic influence makes leadership the property of the group. Now don't smile at this. Go back and read what Cordiner says about a manager's dream of sharing with his associates "a mutually deep vision of what a truly inspired organization can achieve." You see, even Mr. Cordiner is talking like a social scientist.

Most of the other definitions of leadership in your collection are less lofty than Cordiner's, and more directly in line with the basic human-relations doctrines of group participation. A typical one is that definition by Vice President Frederick Macarow of the Chesapeake & Potomac Telephone Co.:

"Leadership is the activity of influencing people to cooperate toward some goal which they come to find desirable." That really makes no bones about calling the leader a manipulator of subordinates. A lot of well-known men have expressed this view; President Eisenhower, for instance, is quoted as saying that leadership is "the art of getting someone else to do something you want done because he wants to do it." The confusion here is that the job of leading is identified with the techniques that may be used by a leader in managing people, but these aren't what make him a leader. Another way to make this distinction would be to say that an industrial leader isn't a kind of executive, but is someone with very special capacities and traits that make for economic and social progress. He's a person who has an innate predisposition for innovation and change, and he can change the beliefs, attitudes, and conduct of other people in ways that produce benefits for a great many people. This may seem like a mouthful, but I think it covers the two big closely connected points about leadership, i.e. a leader changes people and things *so that* many people benefit. This means that a man's motives in pressing for innovation and change may disqualify him as a leader, no matter how noteworthy or notorious he may appear to be. Take old John D. Rockefeller Sr.—he certainly pushed himself and others hard to change the oil industry. He was way out ahead of the pack in demonstrating the power of combining capital so as to do away with what he called "wasteful competition," and this maneuver at the same time unquestionably stepped up the industry's output of oil, as well as of profits and dividends. But John D. didn't do this, it seems clear, with the intention of thus benefiting mankind; he was after power and wealth. Nothing wrong with this, of course; but the intensity of his self-interest disqualifies him as an industrial leader, in my judgment. He had a lot of company too—men like Carnegie,

Frick, Armour, Harriman, *et al.* In fact you've got to look hard to identify any leaders among these old-time industrial giants; even with the help of some historical perspective and a lot of biographical data it's a tough job.

Take the case of Sears, Roebuck & Co. Four men who have headed the company since the early Nineties must, I think, be credited with introducing major innovations in Sears' operations, and each one demonstrated certain kinds of business expertise. But I hold that the two who became best known—Julius Rosenwald and General Robert Wood—were not the industrial leaders the other two were. I think it would be useful to take a closer look at each of these men, so you can see what I mean by the difficulties in identifying leadership. Fortunately, their careers have been spelled out in detail in Sears' massive company history, *Catalogues and Counters,* which Boris Emmet and John Jenck prepared in 1950 under the auspices of the University of Chicago and the Rockefeller Foundation. I've been digging into this tome lately, and find it fascinating.

The four men and their eras that I want to talk about are: Sears' aggressive founder-promoter, Richard W. Sears (1893-1908); Julius Rosenwald (1908-24), who cultivated the customer's confidence; Robert E. Wood (1928-54), who changed the company into a retail chain; and Theodore V. Houser (1954-58), who made Sears, Roebuck a remarkable contributor to the nation's economic stability. It would be hard to imagine four more different men in the same business, yet their different qualities turned out to be highly beneficial to the company, despite the fact that three of the four would probably be considered poor executives today.

Richard Sears was a master adman. He started as a railroad station agent in Minnesota, and in 1886 began selling $12 watches by direct mail for $14 to other station agents who resold them at a nice mark-up, and still undersold the

$25 watches they competed with. Sears wasn't especially original in this; selling by mail had been going on a long time, and since the 1870's Aaron Montgomery Ward and many others had been profiting by their mail-order businesses. Moreover, Sears didn't seem enthusiastic about the watch-selling business; he sold out and tried a year at banking in Iowa and then drifted back into watches by returning to work for his former partner, a watch repairman named Roebuck. However, as the business grew and expanded into jewelry, Sears began to put a Barnum and Bailey flourish into mail-order merchandising techniques. He used money-back guarantees, profit-sharing certificates, and every other appeal he could borrow or think of ("Send no money" was one of his great contributions). But his basic technique was to advertise very low prices, keep his mark-up small, and count on continuous high-pressure advertising to give him a fast turnover. In newspaper and magazine ads, direct-mail letters, and his remarkable catalogues, Sears profusely trumpeted forth the goods offered by "the cheapest supply house on earth." His copy usually was hyperbolic, e.g., "$24.95 buys the best cream separator made in the world"; but the fact remained that the goods nearly always lived up to Sears' flamboyant descriptions. And from Sears' folksy, simple texts, people clearly got the impression that Sears, Roebuck & Co. was completely sincere in its efforts to give the common man an extra good deal. Rural citizens, especially, became convinced that Sears, Roebuck was actually an honest and dependable mail-order house—no small feat when you consider that this was the time when fleecing yokels was a standard business practice.

But the big point about Richard Sears' policies and innovations was that they proved highly beneficial to many people, and hence made him a real leader. His compelling ads developed new and widespread demand and taste for

a vast variety of new products. Farmers who never dreamed
of owning things like banquet lamps, phonographs, bed-
room suites, and fancy boots found they could afford to buy
goods just as up-to-date as those owned by the city slickers,
and the more they saw advertised in Sears' catalogues, the
more they wanted. In additions, Sears' merchandising tactics
made businessmen in the cities, as well as those in the small
towns, spruce up their sales and service policies to compete
with Sears' fascinating catalogue; they often copied Sears'
techniques outright. Sears, in short, improved a lot of American merchandising, and did thousands of customers a large
favor in the bargain.

The man who followed Sears as president was almost his
exact opposite. Julius Rosenwald was the cautious, conservative administrator who kept trying to tone Richard Sears
down and make the business more respectable. Rosenwald
started as a cloak-and-suiter whose Chicago firm had flour-
ished in 1895 by supplying Sears with hundreds of men's
suits. Sears' ads for these, featured at $4.98 C.O.D., typically
brought in orders far faster than Rosenwald and others could
supply the goods. Rosenwald, amazed by Sears' prodigious
salesmanship, promptly gave up his own business to join
Sears that same year when Sears offered Rosenwald and
his brother-in-law a half interest in the firm for $75,000.
Rosenwald, a born administrator, found Sears' promotional
schemes and advertising methods increasingly annoying;
Sears' ads kept bringing in the orders so fast that for ten
years the company's buying and shipping departments were
swamped and snarled in confusion, as sales soared from
three quarters of a million to nearly forty million dollars.

Rosenwald often opposed Sears' proposals, many of which,
like the opening of the first mail-order branch house in
Dallas, eventually proved brilliant marketing successes. The
showdown came when the 1907 depression pinched the

firm's sales and Sears argued intensely for bigger and bigger ads and promotion schemes. Rosenwald insisted on a drastic cost-cutting program. After Rosenwald had won this argument, Sears resigned, and thereafter Sears, Roebuck became a fairly systematized and more respectable concern. Sensitive to criticism of Sears' quality standards, Rosenwald approved the setting up of a testing laboratory to check the quality of suppliers' goods, and a merchandise-inspection system further protected the customer from misrepresentation.

Though Rosenwald showed no capacity for being a real industrial leader, he was often hailed as one. Partly this was because of his renown as a philanthropist who gave away some $60 million with a catholic concern for charities. I suppose it could be argued that Rosenwald's charitable activities demonstrated a kind of leadership in corporate public relations, since the firm's name was usually cited in the announcements of his gifts. This publicity must have benefited Sears and its employees. Personally, however, Rosenwald showed little interest in the welfare of Sears' employees; for example, he strongly disapproved the programs that a pioneering general manager, Elmer Scott, had introduced to train workers, raise morale, and improve employee relations generally. (Scott was eventually transferred to the Dallas branch operation.) Similarly, it was not Rosenwald but a vice president, Albert Loeb, who must be credited with developing Sears' remarkable employee profit-sharing plan in 1916.

As a matter of fact Rosenwald doesn't show up as much of an executive, let alone an industrial leader. The company ran profitably along under Loeb, while Rosenwald absented himself in war jobs in Washington and Europe during World War I, and illness kept him away from Sears until late in 1919. When he took the reins again he found a relaxed management team and lax buying procedures, and the company was riding high on the postwar boom. His retrenchment program eliminated both Sears' testing laboratories and its merchandise-inspection procedures, but he couldn't keep Sears from piling up inventories of overpriced goods. Like nearly everyone else, Rosenwald failed to foresee the crash of 1920-21; though prices were already breaking swiftly by the spring of 1920, Sears paid a 40 per cent stock dividend that slashed its surplus by $30 million. Things got really bad in December, 1921, when Sears, strapped for cash to pay its bank loans and preferred dividend, faced the possibility of being taken over by its bankers.

Then it was that able Vice President Loeb came up with the proposal that Rosenwald rescue the company by pledging some $20 million of his great personal fortune. Rosenwald's response was indicative of his ingrained cautiousness: he turned the idea down, on advice of his own attorneys, despite the arguments of his top men that Sears was not losing customers and would soon be on its feet again. Rosenwald only agreed to go along when an outside attorney whom he respected persuaded him that such a move on his part was a sound investment that would secure the Rosenwald family holdings, then estimated at more than $40 million. Obviously Rosenwald wasn't one for putting his company ahead of his family. Ironically, the press hailed his decision to advance Sears the money as a "pledge of faith" and "an unselfish offering" on the part of a "commercial genius." The deal was that Rosenwald would purchase $12 million worth of the company's Chicago real estate, but would advance only $4 million of this in cash—at 7 per cent interest—the rest being covered by notes on which Rosenwald and his heirs were not to be personally liable. In addition, he gave the company 50,000 shares of his Sears stock, worth $5 million at par, with an option to repurchase this stock at par in three years.

Rosenwald was certainly no genius at handling or choosing executives, as the record of his efforts to pick a successor in 1924 make clear. Like many aging corporation presidents faced with an *Executive Suite* situation, he thought his company needed new blood; he chose to pass over his two long-time colleagues, Vice Presidents Adler and Doering, both of whom expected to succeed him. Instead, Rosenwald asked his son Lessing, then manager of Sears' Philadelphia branch, to get from an executive placement agency the names, ages, and experience of ten prominent railroad vice presidents who were under fifty. Rosenwald had developed an awe for railroad efficiency, apparently as a result of his admiration of Daniel Willard, B. & O.'s president, with whom he had worked during World War I. Rosenwald also wanted a fairly young man who had yet to make his pile, on the grounds that a wealthy executive would have little incentive to pound efficiency into Sears' management. These biases of Rosenwald's were fairly typical of that time; perhaps the most significant thing about such criteria is that they show that he tacitly recognized his own failures, both in putting Sears into good operating shape himself, and in training his subordinates to do so. I find that these are quite common failings of administrators.

Well, Rosenwald eventually found the successor he wanted in Charles Kittle, executive v.p. of the Illinois Central. Kittle proceeded, by rudeness (even to Rosenwald) and ruthless driving, to put the kind of iron discipline into Sears that would be likely to get an executive fired pronto in most big corporations today. But a little over three years later, Kittle died, and Rosenwald found himself once again grappling with the problems of succession. He bungled his way through this time, while contending with the aspirations of four of his vice presidents. One was his son Lessing, who had flatly announced to his father that he would resign if he were not picked as president. This ultimatum was adroitly dissolved by Lessing's mother, who was obviously no novice at handling people; she persuaded her son that the presidency would only be "a sop to his pride," that he would always, as president of Sears, be under his father's shadow, and would get small credit for whatever he himself achieved as "the boss's son." Much better, she told him, to go back to his post in Philadelphia where he and his wife had established their individual roots and recognition. Lessing gave in, and told his father to count him out of the presidential race.

As for the two veteran vice presidents whom Rosenwald had passed over previously, Adler was again ignored, but the other one—Doering, the tough operating v.p.—was seriously considered, along with Vice President Robert E. Wood. Wood was an ambitious, driving, ex-Montgomery Ward executive whom Rosenwald had hired about the time he secured railroader Kittle. We'll get to Wood in a moment, but at this point I think that Rosenwald's handling of Doering, as explained by Lessing Rosenwald, is one for the books. Julius Rosenwald knew that Doering had recently asked the late President Kittle for permission to retire, and had promised Kittle he'd stay on for one more year. After Kittle's sudden death, Doering renewed his request for immediate retirement, thereby giving Rosenwald a chance to bypass him again, gracefully. However, Rosenwald apparently thought he had to find out whether Doering should be considered a candidate for the presidency, for he sent son Lessing to ask whether Doering would stay on if he were elected president. Doering responded that he would indeed reconsider his retirement and remain with Sears if he were elected president. Whereupon Julius Rosenwald made his decision, and within nine days of Kittle's death, the directors announced that Vice President Wood had been elected Sears' president. Not surprisingly, both Adler and Doering at once resigned.

The irony of Rosenwald's decision to choose Wood is that he picked the right man for the wrong reasons. His major reasons apparently were that Wood was younger (forty-nine) and hence could direct the company longer; and that Wood, unlike Doering who was already wealthy, had yet to make his fortune, and so would exhibit more incentive. These are typical "common-sense," administrator's reasons for choosing a president, but they aren't any kind of basis for picking a man who is expected to provide leadership for a big corporation. Rosenwald just wasn't an industrial leader himself, so perhaps he couldn't be expected to identify such a leader when he saw one.

But Rosenwald, curiously enough, *was* a real leader in the field of philanthropy. Not because he and his fund gave away so much money (some $75 million) or because he gave to new causes such as building schools for Negroes in the South; or because he used his gifts to stimulate giving by other rich men and by communities; but because Rosenwald established a new pattern for giving; he stipulated that all the money in the Rosenwald Fund be spent within twenty-five years after his own death (which happened in 1932). He was convinced that each generation ought to look out for its own needy, and also benefit from the wealth its own generation had produced. You can see that the policies of his fund conflict pretty directly with the old ideas of property, personal inheritance, etc. I need scarcely say that this kind of giving remains unpopular; most wealthy people still seem to regard their charitable foundations as quasi-permanent memorials to themselves. Rosenwald's philanthropic policies, however, clearly aimed to change the traditional ways of giving so that they might benefit a great many people, including those of later generations, who, if his policies should become widespread, would not expect to depend on the wealth of their forebears.

Now to get back to Rosenwald's successor, Robert E. Wood. Wood had shown managerial ability over a period of nearly twenty years before he ever met Julius Rosenwald. A West Pointer, he had turned in an extraordinary job of construction during the ten years he'd worked on the Panama Canal as the right-hand man of General Goethals; then he'd directed a railroad in Panama, and as a civilian had served briefly as assistant to a du Pont vice president, and assistant to the president of General Asphalt Co. During World War I, Wood had risen to be acting Quartermaster General, and after the war he joined Montgomery Ward as merchandising manager, then vice president. At Ward, Wood put to use his remarkable grasp of statistics (he even read statistical studies as a hobby) and visualized what was happening to the mail-order market. He spotted trends, e.g., the declining rural population, saw that the spreading of paved roads and automobile traffic was shrinking the need for mail-order services, while at the same time increasing the need for retail stores in suburbia where customers could have ample parking room. Wood also saw that competition from chain stores was getting sharper all the time; he became absolutely positive that the future of the mail-order business lay in shifting over to retail stores, and insisted Ward should expand rapidly that way at once. But Ward's President Merseles disagreed so violently and continually that in 1924 Wood's resignation and the notice of his dismissal by Merseles occurred practically simultaneously.

Shortly thereafter Wood talked with Rosenwald, and the latter seemed nearly as skeptical about Wood's beliefs as Merseles had been; however, that fall, about the same time Rosenwald hired Kittle to be Sears' new president, he got Wood to accept a vice presidency of Sears' factories and retail stores. (Rosenwald tempted both men, incidentally, with the prospects of sharing in a fat bonus soon to be granted to Sears' officers.) Luckily for Sears, Kittle backed Wood's marketing ideas, and Wood at once began putting Sears into the retail business. When Wood became president after Kittle's death in 1928, the number of retail stores jumped from 27 to 192, and the chain grew to over 630 stores during the next twenty years, accounting for about three-fourths of Sears' total sales. Verily, Wood changed the direction and character of Sears' operations in ways that benefited more and more people.

Wood also experimented with some departures from common management practices. He spurned the theory of "span of control" (which limits the number of persons a manager is supposed to be able to direct efficiently); by reducing Sears' management structure to three levels, the number of men each manager had to supervise was greatly increased. Wood hoped that if his retail men could be kept free of close personal supervision they would develop initiative. This early effort at "decentralization," however, soon forced Sears to undertake management-training programs, and the company was experimenting in this field before most other large corporations even began to consider executive personnel a major problem. But experience soon showed that centralized control was imperative, and this led to an increasing emphasis on procedures and rules.

In effect these tight controls made it unnecessary for a manager in the field to display much initiative. So Sears' training programs were modestly aimed at producing personnel of "quality mediocrity," i.e., administrators who are reasonably capable. In this realistic approach to the problem of securing good run-of-the-mill managers, Wood and his personnel men can be credited with leadership in a field that, as I need not tell you, has long been overrun with ambitious schemes and techniques for finding and developing "outstanding executives" and "future leaders." I wonder how long it will be before other large corporations finally concede that topflight executives and industrial leaders cannot be systematically produced. Even if they could be, no one corporation would be able to use more than a very few such men—there's just not enough room for many of them in the modern industrial organization.

So much for Wood's contributions to Sears as a leader, and I hope you're still following me. Now I want to talk about the fourth man, Theodore V. Houser, who put his leadership mark on Sears. In my opinion history may prove him to be the most impressive leader the industry has had so far. Houser followed Wood to Sears from Montgomery Ward, where he had become Wood's assistant soon after Wood got a memorandum from him that ran counter to some official views. Wood found that Houser's thinking paralleled his own; Houser on his own initiative had made studies that led him to conclude, as Wood had, that Sears should adopt a policy of retail store expansion. Similarly, Wood and Houser both thought of ways to develop closer relations with Sears' suppliers, and as chief merchandiser of Sears under Wood, Houser concentrated on devising a remarkable strategy of "basic buying."

In this strategy Sears undertook, in close cooperation with its suppliers, the design of products and careful calculation of four manufacturing components, i.e. materials, labor, overhead, and profit. The aim was to develop low-cost, steadily profitable suppliers; these would be located to save distribution costs, and helped in many other ways—e.g. by research, volume orders, and the elimination of selling costs —to reduce their operating costs. In effect, Houser insisted that suppliers use the profits they made on Sears' orders to improve their plants and products. In all important lines, Sears requires a research program under very specific terms:

both the sums of money to be appropriated and the character of the research problems are agreed upon, and the supplier pays for the program out of a definite apportionment of the unit price. Thus Houser thought of Sears' suppliers as definitely part of Sears' whole structure, with Sears helping each continuously to become more and more efficient as a producer. This is a long, long way from the original mail-order idea of mass buying wherever prices were lowest. Obviously, "basic buying" was a new and major step in establishing the interdependence of large and small firms.

But I think Houser's biggest contribution was his plan for balancing Sears' sales and purchases in various geographic sections of the country. In rural communities especially, Sears had long been criticized for taking money out in mail-order sales without contributing anything in return, as local merchants naturally would. In Mississippi, for example, Houser found that Sears was buying less than $500,-000 a year in the area, while selling in the same area some $8 million or $9 million worth of goods. Houser saw that Sears could do much more good economically if it set up several small plants in a rural area instead of one large plant, such as that vast Appliance Park G.E. has built near Louisville, for instance. Houser proceeded to find out how *small* a plant could be built that would still be efficient; and he developed a special system of cost comparisons and hired manufacturers to make products under Sears' labels and standards. In effect, Houser hired machine time on a cost basis, just as manufacturers hire distribution services on a cost basis. Following this policy, Sears established sources across the country to balance sales and purchases; for example, Sears helped to set up about 100 small factories in the southeast, thereby increasing the size of Sears' purchases in that area, so that they reached approximately the same level as Sears' sales in that area. And wherever Sears has helped to place a factory, the economic health of the community has rapidly improved.

You can see why I think this program of Houser's definitely qualifies him as a leader. The fact that it was a *program* makes his leadership considerably different from the kind that his predecessor, General Wood, demonstrated. Wood, for instance, dramatically expanded Sears into the retail-store business, and changed its internal and external organization in line with the changes in population and marketing that he foresaw; whereas Houser led by carefully planning and developing the means for changing Sears into a new kind of industrial unit that aims at linking the supplier, the distributor, and the customer—the linking to be not only for mutual benefit but for the benefit of the general economy. This is a complex achievement, and I won't blame you if you think my description sounds a bit utopian. But in my opinion Houser's complex kind of top-level leadership seems to be the kind that industry is liable to be getting more and more of.

That's not really surprising, of course, in view of the increasing complexity in all areas of business; but it's easy to forget the point, and to assume that industrial leaders will look and act like those who went before them. In some ways they will be the same—a real leader, for instance, is going to have a vision or cause of some kind, the drive and self-confidence to gain command where he can carry out his ideas, and a great sense of timing. However, there's little use expecting a leader in the electrical business, say, to look and act exactly like that grand old giant, Theodore N. Vail, who brought the vision of the A.T. & T. network to pass. I strongly recommend that you read his biography to see how this bonafide industrial leader behaved; but just remember that a lot of things have changed a lot since his

day. Vail was struggling with crude equipment, crude
methods, and crude businessmen; a leader today will have
to struggle with complex equipment, complex methods, and
more sophisticated businessmen. Leaders have to change,
too.

That doesn't mean, though, that very able executives who
aren't leaders won't go right on exhibiting certain characteristics that others will identify as leadership traits.
Traits like foresight and judgment will probably continue
to be taken as evidence that a manager can lead. It's interesting, I think, that Houser himself seems to have put unusual
emphasis on a subordinate's capacity to think out policy
questions and to set objectives that will lead his company
into a completely new direction. One way Houser spotted
this ability in someone he thought might make a good department head was to ask the man to project a policy line for
the particular department he was being considered for.
Houser thinks this pretty rapidly shows up the kind of thinking a manager is capable of. I found a quote of his on this
the other day: "You don't know a man's mind at all until
you ask him to sit down and write out a five-year plan. Then
is when you find out whether he has the ability to lead, the
imagination, and all that goes with it." He makes it sound
simple. One catch—and it's *not* small—that Houser failed
to mention lies in the leadership capacity of the man who
is trying to judge whethei someone else has the ability to
lead; if the judge himself hasn't a good deal of that capacity,
then his judgment of anyone's ability to lead obviously isn't
going to be worth very much.

Where does all this leave us? I'm not sure, but I hope
I've made at least four points clear: first, that great industrial leaders are exceedingly rare and can be surely identified only with historical perspective; second, that such a
leader is not necessarily a good executive, or a good man-

ager; third, he has a cause or vision propelling him forward;
and fourth, he has an inherent capacity for change and
innovation, and changes people and things *so that* many
people benefit. I'm afraid that these four points aren't going
to be much help to you in picking "the year's outstanding
business leader" for that trade association. On the other
hand, you probably won't be able to convince the other
members of the committee that no businessman today really
qualifies as a leader. But I hope you will throw some large
and prickly doubts on the men that *they* propose, and maybe
even help them get a clearer idea of what a real leader is.
If they do get the idea, you can credit yourself with an act
of leadership; you actually could hasten the day when
intelligent businessmen will become honestly respectful of
leadership. Why, the day might come when your executive
friends would even become angrily embarrassed if anyone
nominated them to be "the leader of the year." But a real
leader, of course, wouldn't be embarrassed; he'd be too
intent on leading to give a damn about the effrontery of his
contemporaries.

Cordially yours,

PHILIP CADMUS

# CHAPTER ELEVEN

# Loyalty, Dedication, and Integrity

*In the accomplished executive there appears a fine balance of traits that sets him apart. Perhaps the most subtle balance is required between his dedication to the corporation and his integrity. These are not simple traits, though such phrases as "a dedicated man" and "a man of absolute integrity" have been indiscriminately applied to businessmen who showed nothing more than simple loyalty and honesty. In comparison, the attainment of dedication and integrity, in balance, is an achievement of character that, in the author's observation, represents the pinnacle of an executive's development. The balance between these two traits is indeed the hallmark of the truly great executive. To understand this balance fully, one would, of course, have to possess it; but its ingredients are familiar in various degrees of simplicity, ranging upward from the qualities of loyalty and honesty.*

*The combination of these two traits has particular pertinence for managers working in the large corporations today. The trait of dedication has often been assumed to mark the man who devotes his whole life to his company, who as one execu-*

*tive put it, "eats, sleeps, and drinks the company."
Similarly the trait of integrity is often assumed to
mark those who are ethical, fair, and incorruptible.
Sometimes integrity is also equated with preserv-
ing one's "individuality." However, these meanings of dedication and integrity change when these
two traits balance each other.*

*In this chapter a seasoned executive who has
recently retired endeavors to describe this singular
achievement to a young manager in his former
company who is "on the make." The younger man,
like many others in his position today, has confused loyalty with conformity, while he has
scarcely thought about his own integrity.*

Mr. Douglas M. Brady
41 Palmetto Drive
Sarasota, Florida

Dear Mr. Brady:

I hope you will pardon this intrusion, but I am writing
you at the suggestion of my Uncle Stanley. He is one of
your greatest admirers, as you probably know, and he says
that you would be in a position to give me the best possible
answers to the question that has been bothering me and
some of my friends here at American Fabricators. We know
you may think we are impertinent to be asking you this way,
but I remember how much I enjoyed listening to you on
both of those hunting trips I took with you and Uncle Stanley two years ago. So now I am hopeful that you may find
time to reply to this letter, and straighten us out on this
question about "company loyalty."

I will try to explain what our argument is about. There are two fellows in the quality control office with me who claim that the only thing a manager has to do to get ahead is to remember to be always loyal to the company. By this they mean not only should he do everything he can to improve his performance for the benefit of the company, but he should always defend the company and all its policies no matter how much he might personally disagree with them. This point about defending the company came up in connection with the company's recent policy that all employees should participate in local political campaigns; we are asked to express ourselves clearly in public on current issues including high taxes, government-in-business, and labor monopolies. Frankly, this policy is not setting too well with me and several of the other fellows in our executive-development program, but when we questioned it during one of the discussion periods, our conference leader side-stepped the issue by asking if we would mind holding our question "for another time." We acquiesced, but later some of us got to talking it over, and the arguments that resulted have only succeeded in confusing me. The funny thing is that all of us who disagree with the company's new policy are Republicans and agree pretty much with what President Eisenhower and the party have been doing in Washington. But we don't like the idea of being asked by the company to participate in local politics. We think that's our private concern, and that loyalty to the company just doesn't go that far.

The more I've thought about it, the more I've concluded that this idea of the "dedicated man" who puts the company first, before everything else, is not for me. In my opinion, a man who will let a company dominate his personal life to that extent isn't much of a man. I suspect that every manager who says he would always put his company first is only kidding himself. From what I've seen of the managers in American Fabricators they're pretty much interested in only two things: how much money they make and what their titles are. Furthermore, I'm sure that most of them are ready to do anything the company asks them to simply because they're afraid not to; they're afraid they might be considered "queer," and not "one of the boys," and this might mean they wouldn't be considered "one of the team," as that employee booklet they handed us describes it. Personally I think that being loyal to the company because you're really afraid not to be is too high a price to pay for the security of a job and a pension from the company.

There have been a good many times recently when I seriously considered quitting the company to try my luck somewhere else. However when this discussion about company loyalty came up, I began to think that maybe I was being immature about the matter, and ought to talk to someone who has been "through the mill," as they say, and really knows what it takes to succeed at American Fabricators. I guess you can see that that's why I'm writing this letter to you. Anything you care to say on this subject will be deeply appreciated.

Respectfully,<br>RANDOLPH STEWART

Mr. Randolph Stewart
Quality Control Division
American Fabricators, Inc.
Newark, New Jersey

Dear Randy:

It was good to hear from you. It's been some time since those hunting trips, and I didn't know you had joined American Fabricators. Your Uncle Stanley never told me, and as you perhaps know, I haven't been in touch with things at the company too much since my retirement a year ago last July. Your letter made me realize how quickly things can change after you've stepped down to let others handle your job. The questions you raise about loyalty to the company and the new policy about participating in local politics are important questions, and I am very glad, for your sake, that you are raising them. I can't promise to give you any black and white answers, but I will try to show you what my experience has taught me to think and believe about such matters.

I'll start off with your question about loyalty to the company, because if you get yourself cleared away on this point the problem raised by the company's new policy ought to take care of itself. Loyalty happens to be one of the necessary ingredients to any organization. If the members of an organization aren't loyal to it in some degree, the organization doesn't really exist; it's merely a loose association of people mostly held together by a payroll and fringe benefits. But of course you don't get loyalty just by asking for it; the members have to be convinced that a company deserves their loyalty. They want assurance that the company's products and services are O.K., and if possible they want their company to be performing some kind of useful function, like feeding, clothing, and housing, or improving the standards of living or of information, etc., etc. I think you'll agree that American Fabricators meets several of these tests of usefulness; most large corporations do—that's one reason they're large, of course.

This is the minimum basis for company loyalty, and by itself it isn't enough to ensure the strong allegiance of people. But along with decent pay and pleasant surroundings it seems to be enough to satisfy a great many employees. At least I've found that it's unrealistic to expect most employees to develop more than a mild sort of loyalty to their company, unless the company takes some special measures, such as extra-liberal personnel policies, or in some cases profit sharing. Even then I think the management of a company is fooling itself if it believes that such measures will generate great and lasting loyalty. Too many other companies today are prepared to compete for the employee's loyalty on these material terms. Much more powerful, in my judgment, are the intangible measures a company can take to win support. These include such difficult things as becoming the most respected and successful firm in its field, and developing the kind of managers that in turn develop an *esprit de corps*. Yet even these unusual achievements won't guarantee a man's loyalty. The only one who can do that is the man himself.

If you are going to become intensely loyal to American Fabricators you've got to be "sold" on the company; you've got to feel you're a part of it and be ready to defend it to outsiders who may criticize it. You've got to become prejudiced about it, in some degree, and convinced that its products are as good as—or better than—the company says they are. If you can do all this, it means, in effect, that there are no major differences between the objectives and values the company upholds and those that you uphold. If the company policy, for instance, is to make as good a product as can be made at a cost that will ensure a certain return on its investment, and if you, on the other hand, believe the company should always try to make the highest grade product on its market, then you don't agree with the company's objective, and you can't be truthfully loyal to it.

However, right here I want to caution you that loyalty has its pitfalls, and one of them is the tendency of very loyal people to go blind. Often the "dedicated man" you refer to isn't motivated by an idealistic sense of service or by complete agreement with the company's objectives and standards. Frequently it's only his fear of being demoted or fired that moves a man to approve everything his company does; or he may simply lack the perspective to see that his company's policies are shortsighted and stupid; or again, he may be apathetic to the opportunities his company offers him, and merely seek to follow routines without questioning them. Quite often, it seems to me, the super-loyal manager, i.e., the man who is willing to put the company's interests ahead of every other interest he has, is trying to punish himself for some imagined mistake, or some failing he exaggerates in himself. Anyway, I've seen a good many of these men get to the top of their companies through the sheer devotion of all their energies to the company, night and day—and when they got to the top they weren't equipped to provide what the situation called for, such as a major change in objectives.

I guess that's the biggest pitfall of loyalty, and I don't know that I can do more than just point it out to you, for if you ever let your loyalty go that far, it's not likely that any of your colleagues will be able to make you see what you're doing to yourself. Some years ago I got to know the president of a successful small company who had literally given all his time and energy to the company. When the company was bought out by a large corporation, he became executive vice president of the corporation, but some of the policies he'd fought for and developed in the small company were automatically canceled by the merger. For instance, his policy of uncompromising quality control on every item was scrapped in favor of a random inspection check of finished lots. Similarly, the big corporation's labor policies were handled by lawyers instead of by face-to-face negotiations between union leaders and top officers. After about a year of struggling to accept the situation, this executive—who had been, in his old situation, a fine manager—went to pieces and shot himself. His intense devotion to the small company had made him incapable of adapting to standards he considered lower than his own. This is an extreme example, of course, but I have seen many other men whose managerial abilities became withered or crippled when they were forced to adopt lower standards or follow a policy they didn't really believe in.

That's why I suggest you take time now, while you're young, to try to clarify at least some of your own standards and values and objectives in business. You'll undoubtedly change these as you grow up, but the pain of learning better should develop your own strengths, whereas if you're vague about what you think is worth working hard for, you may begin to accept any and all company standards or objectives for the sake of expediency or "harmony." That habit can turn a man into a jellyfish, which is, I remind you, also a blind creature. Let's assume that one of your worth-while objectives is honestly to try to make the company a better organization for serving its customers. If you thought about this some, you might expand your objective to make the company better for serving the company's suppliers and the general public. That might make you examine the company's operations and policies much more closely, and you would undoubtedly find things to criticize. And if you're really loyal to the company you will criticize as best you can; that is, criticize wherever you have thought out a constructive proposal to offer as a corrective. If you haven't thought out such a proposal, then you'd better keep quiet, or else keep your criticism muffled in the form of intelligent questions.

At the same time, your loyalty can be measured by the way you recognize your obligation to cover up the company's weaknesses. I mean those weaknesses that a company may have acquired just by being in a particular industry or subject to certain conditions. If the company was in an extremely competitive industry, for example, you might show loyalty by not selling out to any rival company that made the highest bid for your services. In a low-paying industry you would be loyal if you were willing to work overtime to get the work out. And if you worked for a government agency you would show your loyalty by adhering strictly to the rules that have been laid down in such bureaucracies in order to keep them operating steadily with mediocre personnel. No matter what kind of organization you worked for, you would be loyal if you managed to give something more to the job than is expected of you.

However, it is this matter of giving something extra to the job that brings up the subject of extracurricular activities, like participating in local politics, which American Fabricators is now asking you to do. Here, as you can see, the company policy assumes that such outside participation by its managers will improve its public and community relations and also perhaps develop the political skills of its managers. A still broader objective of these political activities would be to benefit industry in general by having businessmen publicly champion the views they believe will benefit the economy. I am not passing judgment on these aims, just stating them. The decision as to whether you can accept them has to be your own decision. The question is quite simple: does your sense of loyalty to the company go as far as these objectives, or doesn't it? But getting the answer is not simple, for the answer depends on your understanding of yourself and of your relationship to the company as a young manager.

From what you've written me, it is clear that you have already begun to challenge the company's right to ask you to participate in local politics; you think this is your private concern, and that the company is asking too much of you. I wonder if that's really why you and some of your friends object to the policy? Isn't it possible that all of you are rationalizing, and that what you actually object to is that others, outside and inside the company, may assume you are a company stooge if you do get into politics actively now? If you haven't done much thinking about political issues, you *would* be stooges if you simply took the political line you thought the company would approve. But if you've really thought through your political convictions, then loyalty to the company could mean accepting the new policy and going out and supporting those convictions the company publicly supports. And if you don't agree at all with something in the company's political line, then I think you should abstain from political action in public that would embarrass the company. Every manager is obligated to do this as a responsible member of his company's management; but a good manager would not abstain simply because he knows, from a practical standpoint, that top management expects him to. (I need scarcely say that a manager who publicly espoused political views his co-managers did not share would not be likely to get to the top echelons.) A good manager would abstain because he is being paid as a manager to help his company, not to embarrass it or openly oppose its official views. By accepting payment for his services, he becomes obligated, simply as a man of integrity who intends to deal honestly with his company, to refrain from behavior that could impair his value as a manager by casting doubt on his integrity. By integrity here I mean what has wisely been called "the honesty of intention."

On the other hand, a manager of integrity would continue to feel free to speak his views *privately* on any matter, including any that might not be approved by his company; but in every such case he would have to have the discrimination to know whether he is being heard confidentially as an individual, or whether he is being heard publicly as a manager whose personal views might prove harmful to his company. Keeping the fine line of distinction between these two roles is often so difficult that a manager may choose never to express any views he knows the company would not approve—but a good manager will develop the necessary discrimination.

At the same time, you shouldn't ever forget that your commitment to serve the company isn't your first commitment. What you put ahead of the company will depend on your own values, of course—maybe you would place your family, or your religion, or your country, ahead of American Fabricators. If you do, most people would agree with you. But I will tell you right now that I don't consider any of these your first obligation; and I will add that until you discover what your first obligation is, you won't, in my opinion, ever know the most important meaning of dedication. What's more, you won't know the full meaning of integrity.

However, I think I've written much more than enough in answer to your inquiry. I'll end this here with the hope that I haven't confused you too much about company loyalty. Please give my best to your Uncle Stanley, and tell him I'm looking forward to seeing him down here again this year.

Sincerely,

Douglas M. Brady

Mr. Douglas M. Brady
41 Palmetto Drive
Sarasota, Florida

Dear Mr. Brady:

I don't know how to thank you for your letter. I've been thinking about it and re-reading it ever since I received it, and I think I'm a great deal clearer than I was about my loyalty to American Fabricators. I've now decided I'm going to lend a hand to the Republican campaign committee in my district, but will keep some of my views to myself—such as my conviction that industry ought to stop its incessant yammering for lower taxes. I don't agree with the N.A.M. line that American Fabricators has been following, for instance. Also, I think that Eisenhower, as a leader, should have come out boldly in favor of giving birth-control information and assistance to overpopulated nations, because as I see it every nation is just going to have to insist on birth control in the face of this "population explosion." However, I can see that if I express these views publicly it might embarrass the company—and you've made me realize that this contradicts my obligation to serve the company. But I am hoping that someday I'll be in a position to help change some of the company's thinking on political matters.

Most of what you've written me about company loyalty I am ready to agree with, but in thinking over the idea of dedication to a company I don't see how a manager can put his company ahead of his family or his religion or his country. I've tried to think what could be more important than any of these, and guess maybe you meant that one's first obligation should be to humanity—that is, to contributing to the improvement of human welfare in whatever ways we can. I could accept this all right.

Still, I don't get what you added about "integrity"—what has this got to do with being dedicated to some high goal? The only connection I can see is that having integrity means being honest, and if you weren't honestly dedicated to your goal, you wouldn't have integrity. But I've got a feeling that that may not be what you meant, and I would be most grateful if you would clear up this point for me. . . .

Respectfully,
RANDOLPH STEWART

Mr. Randolph Stewart
Quality Control Division
American Fabricators, Inc.
Newark, New Jersey

Dear Randy:

Your response to that long letter I wrote you about loyalty makes me feel that perhaps I said too much, and took too much for granted, also. However, I think you have hold of the main idea I tried to get across about obligation, and that should be helpful. Your decision on the political activities sounds all right to me, at any rate, and I also think your views on taxes and birth control are well taken. I needn't warn you that you may not find these views popular among your colleagues, but this shouldn't worry you.

I'm glad I puzzled you about what should be your first obligation. It's easy to say there are bigger things in life than helping to make a corporation successful, and that money isn't everything, but as a manager you will continue to find your obligations to your company extremely important for a long spell, and if you're going to be a good manager you will just naturally expect to be rewarded handsomely. However, in guessing that I meant your first obligation ought to be to help improve human welfare you were completely wrong. I know you've heard some supposedly wise people say this is what everyone should do, but that doesn't make it so, of course, and the way I understand things, all these high-sounding humanitarian goals are beside the point. They're even worse than that, I think, because they allow people to evade the main point, which is that your first obligation is *to your own self*. That won't sound selfish to you if you think it through. Unless you accept responsibility for yourself, and work to develop yourself, you can't rightly begin to help anyone else.

Now take this matter of dedication in a manager. I think you can see how a man who gives himself totally to his corporation, night and day, is refusing to take responsibility for his own development. He's literally sacrificing himself for the company, and the more he sacrifices this way the less valuable he becomes to the company—in the long run, if not sooner. It can show up in small ways as well as large. If he doesn't learn how to relax, i.e., take the responsibility for learning how to relax, both on and off the job, for instance, he's going to produce tensions in others that will hurt both him and his company. If he doesn't study his own behavior and its effect on others, and temper his actions accordingly, he's likely to make trouble for everyone, including himself. In other words, in his dedication to the company, he's got to be increasingly conscious of himself and responsible for himself, especially in his relation to his associates.

As a manager, he should be clear about his obligations to work for the company's objectives. And when he discharges these obligations, he shows his loyalty to this mutual relationship. But he should also be clear about the company's obligation to him. If the company fails to discharge these, he no longer owes it his loyalty. How does a company fail? I think mostly by not requiring the manager to give his best performance; by making it easy for him to avoid responsibility and toughening experiences; by rewarding him generously with a bonus or stock option when he has done nothing special to deserve these. And the manager fails, of course, in succumbing to such treatment by the company. He does this, I should judge, most often because it is easy, comfortable, and reassuring to do so; both his pride and his sense of security become pleasantly inflated. When this happens, however, he is on his way to losing something extremely precious to him— nothing less, in fact, than his own integrity.

Now I think you will see what I mean by integrity, and why it's so very closely tied up with loyalty and dedication.

You have an obligation to be loyal to a company; and this is based on a mutual relationship; this state holds so long as both you and the company discharge your obligations to each other. But above all, your dedication to the company is governed by the way you discharge your first obligation, which is to yourself. If the company fails to meet its obligations to you as a manager, then it forfeits your loyalty, and you in turn could not remain dedicated to the company if you were determined to retain your integrity.

There's much more I might say about integrity, but maybe I'd better stop here and wait until I hear from you. I hope at any rate that what I've said about dedication makes some sense to you.

Sincerely,<br>DOUGLAS M. BRADY

Mr. Douglas M. Brady
41 Palmetto Drive
Sarasota, Florida

Dear Mr. Brady:

You gave me lots to think about in that last letter you sent me. I'm especially grateful for your helping me to realize that my first obligation is actually to myself. This has cleared up for me most of the stuff I've been studying lately about human relations in industry. The way some of these sociologists carry on about group activity, one gets the idea that the individual isn't worth bothering about, since he'll get all the satisfactions and experience he needs just by "participating" with the group. Unfortunately, I'm afraid several of the executives at American Fabricators seem to have taken this message as the gospel truth; or perhaps they may think it's simply a sophisticated way to get cooperation from the employees.

The points you made about the ways that both the man-

ager and the company can fail in their obligations to each
other have given me an entirely new slant on loyalty and
dedication. I hope I can manage to apply what you've said,
especially the point about taking responsibility for my own
behavior. I'm going to watch out that I don't sacrifice everything in my personal life for the sake of American Fabricators. I expect the hardest thing, though, will be to resist succumbing to the company's kind treatment, including such
things as a nice raise I don't really earn. If I should turn
down a raise because I thought I didn't deserve it, the boys
around here would sure give me the horse laugh. But maybe
I've misunderstood what you said about this? If so, I guess I
just didn't grasp your remarks about integrity, for I still
am of the opinion that integrity concerns one's honesty and
ethics. I would greatly appreciate it if you could give me
some examples of integrity in industry that would illustrate
what you meant.

Once again, I wish to thank you for your willingness to
continue this correspondence with me. I hope you will be
patient with my questions, some of which must sound pretty
silly.

Respectfully,<br>RANDOLPH STEWART

Mr. Randolph Stewart
Quality Control Division
American Fabricators, Inc.
Newark, New Jersey

Dear Randy:
You need never apologize for asking questions if you're
really serious about learning. That's the way you'll learn the
fastest, and as you've probably guessed, there's nothing an
old man like me likes better than to answer questions he

thinks he's qualified to answer. What's more, I'm probably getting more out of this correspondence than you are, though I won't bother to explain why.

Now let's have another try at this matter of integrity. You asked for some examples to help clarify the subject, and I guess the best examples I can give you come right from my own experience with American Fabricators. In talking to you about them, of course, I am entrusting you with information that some of my old associates are unaware of, and you will appreciate that I don't wish to embarrass them or the company.

Let's start with the problem of executive bonuses and the lesson I learned from my predecessor, Tom Daniels, years ago, just before I succeeded him as president of American Fabricators. He called me into his office and asked me, in a half-joking manner, what was the first major change I proposed to make when I took over his job. I told him the one I had in mind at the moment was the adoption of an incentive bonus plan for executives, since I thought this might quickly win my associates' cooperation, and make them eager to do their best for the company. Daniels looked surprised, I recall, and asked me if I had studied the results of the plan the company had used about fifteen years before. I had to admit I hadn't, since this was before I would have been eligible for such a bonus.

Daniels then pulled a folder out of his desk drawer and showed me an analysis of the plan he had had the treasurer draw up. It showed that over a period of twenty years large bonuses had been paid to about twenty-five top managers. It also showed, as Daniels immediately pointed out, that the bonuses were figured as a straight percentage of each manager's salary, and though this percentage varied occasionally, I saw that it bore no rational relation to the yearly fluctuations in the company's sales and profits. The bonuses either went up each year, or stayed the same, but they never dropped, even though American Fabricators lost money in seven of the twenty years. Daniels asked me what I thought of this old plan, and I told him it looked very unfair, since the bonuses were paid out even when the company was unprofitable. Daniels agreed emphatically, saying he considered the payments downright dishonest. He said he tried to change the plan when he became president by omitting bonuses in any year the company didn't earn 5 per cent on its investment. However, Daniels soon concluded that the worst thing about the plan was that the bonuses were rigidly related to salaries instead of approximately related to each manager's contribution to American Fabricators during each year.

Daniels told me he had for years taken his bonuses for granted as a more or less fixed and major part of his income, and he was sure everyone else in the company did likewise. He tried to work out a rating system of points on which bonus payments could be based, but he couldn't get one that satisfied him. Finally he gave up and accepted the old system of bonuses as a fixed percentage of salary. But he couldn't quite manage to forget his conviction that awarding bonuses according to the merit of the individual manager is the only valid basis on which they can be awarded. That standard, that idea, kept bothering him; he said it made him feel dishonest every time he approved the list of bonuses. After two years of battling his conscience, he abolished the whole bonus plan. It was the only way, he said, that he "could live with himself."

When Daniels finally asked me if I thought I could live with myself in administering my proposed bonus plan, I couldn't answer him, and felt embarrassed. That night, I sat down by myself and tried to think through my own position on the bonus problem. I realized that what Daniels meant when he said he couldn't "live with himself" was that he couldn't let himself do something which he had come to see as a dishonest act. He recognized that by dispersing extra rewards *which had not been earned by extra executive efforts and positive results,* he was, as president, wasting the funds of the corporation. In doing that, he was false to the trust placed in him by the directors and stockholders of American Fabricators. In a man like Daniels, such behavior would obviously conflict with the qualities his character had developed—especially such traits as trustworthiness, forthrightness, and what Daniels used to call "moral and ethical conduct based on religious principles." In other words, Daniels had his own sense of his whole character, and this eventually made it impossible for him to allow one weak trait to upset his other qualities. He was honest with himself; he saw that his integrity was breached in this matter of bonuses to the extent at least that he did not do his best to give to each man—including himself—his just due. The extreme difficulty of doing this, of course, is one reason why over half the large corporations in the country still do not pay executive bonuses.

For my part, the lesson Daniels taught me about bonuses was my first big lesson in integrity. I hope it's helpful to you, too. However, you won't learn what integrity is just from one lesson. In fact, I found I didn't recognize a big lack of integrity in myself until shortly before I retired from American Fabricators. It wasn't bonuses this time (I discarded my plan, needless to say) but extracurricular activities that gave me this painful lesson. In the last five years of my term as president and chairman of American Fabricators, my outside activities had included the following: the honorary presidency of a national health agency; the presidencies of two state organizations (civil liberties and soil conservation); membership on the executive committees of four local groups (school board, taxpayers' association, city council, and chamber of commerce); plus three different assignments with the federal government. In addition, I was at one time director of fourteen corporations, and in my last three years with American Fabricators I averaged perhaps fifteen speeches a year to large gatherings and a dozen or so informal talks to small groups. Most of my speaking was about the businessman's responsibility in economic and political issues, such as free enterprise and foreign trade.

In undertaking all this activity I naturally had to spread myself pretty thin, but I was enjoying it a great deal. At first I was pleased that well-known organizations wanted me as a speaker; I guess the gratification of having a crowd of people listen to me talk was something I always wanted, and in the first year I really worked very hard at my speeches. The result was I was asked to address still more organizations, and eventually it appears that I got on some kind of list as being available and willing to speak on a variety of subjects. By then I had become quite dependent on two young men in our public-relations department who proved themselves very skillful in drafting speeches for me. After talking with me for as little as five minutes on a subject, they could turn out a rough draft that for the most part embodied my ideas. To keep myself posted on current issues and problems, I read a great many books in addition to articles in the *Atlantic Monthly, Harper's,* the *Foreign Affairs Quarterly, Fortune,* the *Harvard Business Review,* and similar publications. I really think I became what might be called a force-cultivated businessman.

Fortunately, during these years two of my vice presidents proved themselves so capable that I assumed I could leave the running of American Fabricators entirely in their hands. Anyway, I spent more and more time on outside activities. I recall that one day my secretary, Ann Marshall, estimated

I was averaging about forty hours a week on various extra-curricular functions. This surprised me, for it meant I was only spending about ten hours a week on American Fabricators' affairs. But this didn't bother me; I felt justified in becoming a nationally known businessman for the sake of my company. I guess my justification was mainly based on the words of Owen D. Young, who once said that his main role as chairman of the General Electric Company was "to be known." I accepted—rather uncritically I'm afraid—the idea that the better known to the public the chief officer of a corporation becomes, the better will be the public relations of the corporation. It was not until later that I had to admit I didn't think that the public recognition accorded to me had really done anything for American Fabricators beyond vaguely identifying it as a company whose managers seem very interested in their relations with the outside world.

However, I really woke up to what I was doing, and not doing, one evening about a year before I retired. I had appeared at a dinner where I was to speak without having had time to read the draft of the speech the two public-relations chaps had prepared for me. While the toastmaster discussed other matters with the audience, I tried to shuffle quickly through the pages as I held them in my lap behind the speaker's table. The speech was to be on "The Role of the Businessman in Middle East Politics," and it had been based, at my suggestion, on some facts and ideas I had read in a U.N. publication. But as I scanned the draft I realized I actually didn't understand several of the ideas the public-relations writers had inserted. It wasn't their fault, for I simply hadn't found time to sit down and go over the subject with them as I usually did. However, that evening I saw that, even if I had done so, I would have simply been rehashing other people's ideas, and taking credit for them. The fact jolted me; I just wasn't qualified to speak on this subject. And then I

realized how many other previous times I had publicly presented as mine material that had been thought out and
prepared by others. This disturbed me so much that when I
finally rose to speak I tossed the prepared speech aside and
openly confessed the embarrassing position I was in; then
I plunged ahead and extemporized a talk about businessmen and politics. It wasn't very good, but it was all my own,
and I felt good about it. From then on, I vowed I would
never again accept an invitation to speak unless I felt qualified by my own experience and knowledge to do so. In addition, I avowed to prepare the complete text of my own
speech myself.

As I now see it, my willingness to let others prepare my
speeches was only the most obvious evidence of my lack of
integrity. I realize that executives are rarely good speech
writers, but this does not make the use of ghost writers an
honorable practice. In my present judgment, any man who
will present the work of others as his own, as I so often did,
cannot be credited with integrity; but my integrity was also
impaired in less obvious ways. I began to realize that my
absorption in extracurricular activities had put me seriously
out of touch with my own industry, and with my associates
in the corporation. As chief officer, I should have continued
to be predominantly interested in American Fabricators, and
have limited my outside interests accordingly. The trouble
was that when I started participating in community affairs,
then in national and philanthropic organizations, I felt more
and more caught by the responsibilities I assumed. Perhaps
it would be more accurate to say that I felt more and more
reluctant to withdraw from positions I had publicly assumed.

I don't want to sermonize on the highly debatable issue
of "community relations." How much responsibility for
community relations the modern corporation and its executives should assume is a large and tricky question. However,

I've been thinking about this a good deal since receiving your last letter, and I've tried to educate myself specifically on how much outside participation by a high-ranking manager can be justified in terms of his own integrity. I have been reading some of the writings of Plato, Aristotle, and Kant, in an effort to clarify some of my own thinking about integrity, and I keep going back to the words of Socrates on the meaning of justice. In one passage, which you may remember, he says that justice is the principle that "one man should practice one thing only, the thing to which his nature was best adapted." He also says that "justice is doing one's own business, and not being a busybody." These ideas have led me to conclude that when I was active as chief executive officer of American Fabricators, in my outside activities and speeches I was not "doing my own business," but trying to be something other than a businessman. I guess I fancied myself as a kind of business statesman. In any case, I am persuaded now that I continued to accept my salary of $200,000 a year, plus my secretary's services and the use of the company's mailing and mimeographing facilities, while engaging in activities that I now consider only slightly contributive to the company. I think these activities contributed almost entirely to my own self-interest, or *amour propre*, as the French say.

This problem of self-interest is the heart of the manager's whole problem, in my opinion. It is the kind of self-interest that either makes or breaks a manager as he rises in the company. As I see it, a young would-be executive has got to start out with a lot of personal ambition for money and power, but at some point he'll have to shift his center of interest from wanting things for himself to wanting to develop his own potentials. You can call both of these self-interest, but they're entirely different in effect and purpose. Unless you achieve the second kind of self-interest, Randy,

you won't really know what integrity is, in the way I meant
to describe it in this letter. Also, your sense of loyalty to the
company takes on a different limitation when your attitude
toward yourself shifts. Once you've become aware of the
central importance of your integrity, you will be loyal to
American Fabricators only so long as you think this company is the best place for you to fulfill your capacities. You
will regard the company not as an organization to be feared
or loved or bowed down to, but as a vehicle for your own
development. And by then you should be smart enough to
consider the tough spots and frustrations of corporate life as
being potentially very good for you. On the other hand, the
blandishments, security, and rewards that the company pre-
sents you with you will regard as potentially dangerous to
your growth. At the same time, your dedication to the company will include both this intelligently limited kind of loyalty and the sense of integrity that keeps you from becoming
lopsided and obsessed with your own importance.

What I've said about this shift to another kind of self-
interest may sound idealistic or impractical to you, because
you're still very young in the management game. But as
you pick up more experience, I surely hope you will achieve
this shift, for there's no chance for a man to become a great
executive without it. It is what always separates the men
from the boys. You won't be able to fake this shift; and you
won't achieve it unless you have already developed a wide
range of qualities. As you acquire these, you should become
what Socrates called "the just man." In what is now one of
my favorite passages, Socrates says that justice is concerned
"not with the outward man but with the inward, which is
the true self and concernment of man. For the just man does
not permit several elements within him to interfere with one
another, or any of them to do the work of others—he sets in

order his inner life and is his own master and his own law, and at peace with himself."

These words are the best definition I have ever seen of what it takes to become a great executive. Needless to say, there are very, very few such men in management, or anywhere else, for that matter. But in my judgment the best goal you could shoot for in your career would be to work to qualify for membership in this select group. Even if you don't make the grade, I can assure you that the process of trying will do more to make an executive out of you than anything I know of.

Sincerely,
DOUGLAS M. BRADY

*Set in Linotype Caledonia*
*Format by Dorothy S. Kaiser*
*Manufactured by American Book-Stratford Press*
*Published by Harper & Brothers, New York*